Horizons

Mathematics 1

Book 2

by
Sareta A. Cummins

Edited by
David J. Korecki

Illustrated by
Tye A. Rausch

Editorial Staff
Christine A. Korecki
John P. Robinett

Alpha Omega Publications, Inc.
Rock Rapids, Iowa

Horizons Mathematics 1, Book 2 is only a *part* of a mathematics curriculum which consists of Horizons Mathematics 1, Book 1; Horizons Mathematics 1, Book 2; and Horizons Mathematics 1 Teacher's Guide. It is *necessary* to use the Teacher's Guide for a complete first grade mathematics program. The Teacher's Guide contains some essential concepts that are not presented in the student books.

Horizons Mathematics 1, Book 2
© MCMXCI by Alpha Omega Publications, Inc. ® All rights reserved.
804 N. 2nd Ave., E., Rock Rapids, IA 51246-1759

ISBN 978-1-58095-930-8

Printed in the United States of America

Horizons

Mathematics 1

PLACE VALUE – ONE HUNDREDS

1 The number 135 has three places.
The 1 is in the hundreds' place.
The 3 is in the tens' place. The 5
is in the ones' place.

hundreds' place
tens' place
ones' place

1 3 5

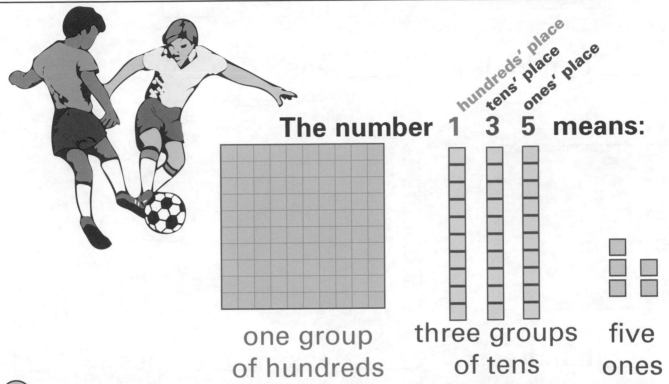

The number 1 3 5 means:

hundreds' place
tens' place
ones' place

one group
of hundreds

three groups
of tens

five
ones

2 Count the hundreds. Count the tens. Count the
ones. Write the numbers.

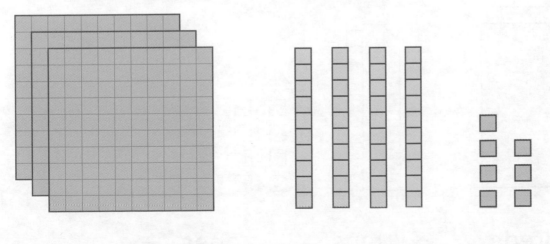

_____ hundreds   _____ tens   _____ ones = _____

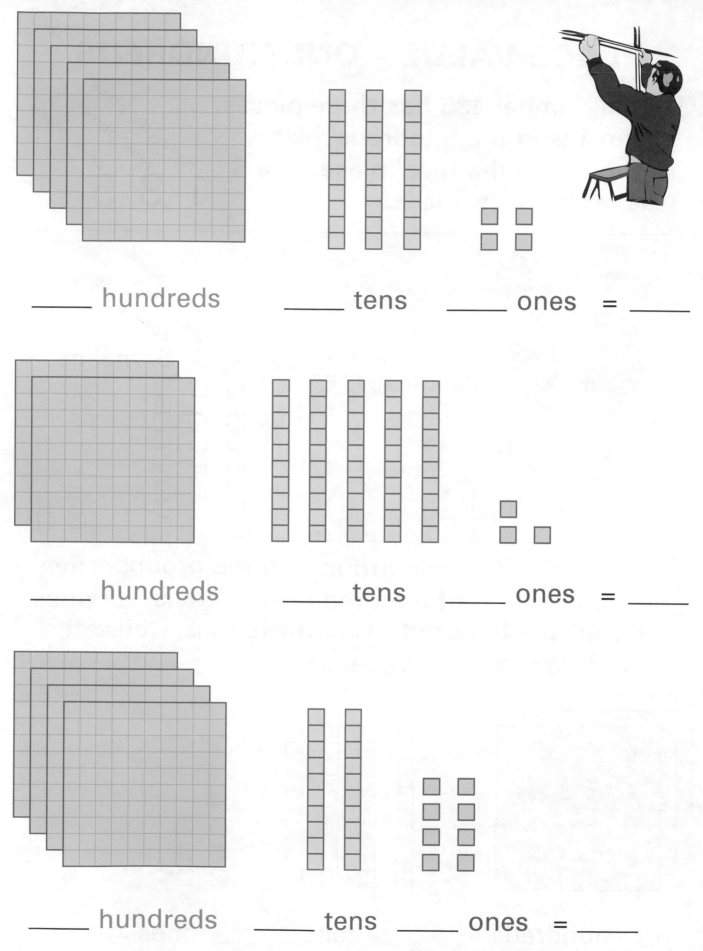

_____ hundreds _____ tens _____ ones = _____

_____ hundreds _____ tens _____ ones = _____

_____ hundreds _____ tens _____ ones = _____

2

③ Circle the correct answer.

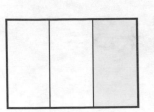   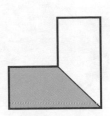 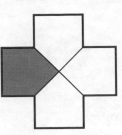

$\frac{1}{2}$ $\frac{1}{3}$ $\frac{1}{4}$ $\frac{1}{2}$ $\frac{1}{3}$ $\frac{1}{4}$ $\frac{1}{2}$ $\frac{1}{3}$ $\frac{1}{4}$ $\frac{1}{2}$ $\frac{1}{3}$ $\frac{1}{4}$ $\frac{1}{2}$ $\frac{1}{3}$ $\frac{1}{4}$

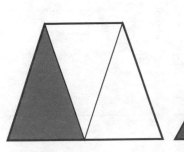 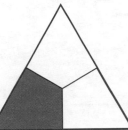 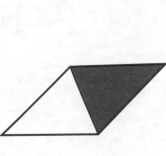 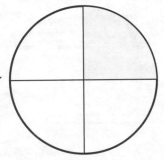

$\frac{1}{2}$ $\frac{1}{3}$ $\frac{1}{4}$ $\frac{1}{2}$ $\frac{1}{3}$ $\frac{1}{4}$ $\frac{1}{2}$ $\frac{1}{3}$ $\frac{1}{4}$ $\frac{1}{2}$ $\frac{1}{3}$ $\frac{1}{4}$

④ Write the answers.

How many inches is the longest side?
_____ inches

How many inches is the shortest side?
_____ inches

How many inches is the third side?
_____ inches

What is the distance around the
triangle? _____ inches

⑤ **Write the subtraction facts.**

6+1=7	2+6=8	4+3=7
_____	_____	_____
_____	_____	_____
7+2=9	2+5=7	1+7=8
_____	_____	_____
_____	_____	_____

⑥ **Subtract.**

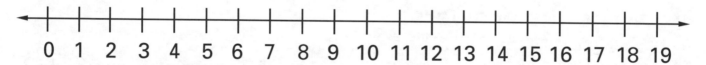

0 1 2 3 4 5 6 7 8 9 10 11 12 13 14 15 16 17 18 19

10 - 2	13 - 4	14 - 6	11 - 3	13 - 8	10 - 6

12 - 5	15 - 7		11 - 9	14 - 7

4

SHAPES

circle

square

triangle

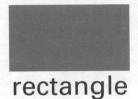
rectangle

(1) Color the circle red.

Color the triangle blue.

Color the square yellow.

Color the rectangle green.

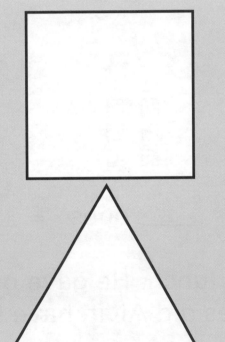

(2) Write the number.

twenty-six _____   ninety-five _____

fifty-two _____   thirty-three _____

seventy-four _____   eighty-seven _____

thirteen _____   sixty-nine _____

5

3 **Write the numbers.**

_____ hundreds   _____ tens   _____ ones   =   _____

_____ hundreds   _____ tens   _____ ones   =   _____

4 Alvin had three cookies for lunch. He gave one to Lewis. How many cookies did Alvin have left?

_____ - _____ = _____ _____

Norma had 7 pencils. She broke the lead on 3. How many pencils did Norma have left that she could use?

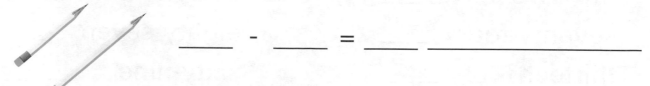

_____ - _____ = _____ _____

6

COUNTING – TWO HUNDRED

① **Write the number that comes between.**

165	___	167	134 ___ 136	

165 ___ 167   134 ___ 136

127 ___ 129   142 ___ 144

150 ___ 152   176 ___ 178

② **Write the number.**

124 has a _____ in the ones' place.

421 has a _____ in the ones' place.

142 has a _____ in the tens' place.

412 has a _____ in the tens' place.

241 has a _____ in the hundreds' place.

142 has a _____ in the hundreds' place.

③ **Write the subtraction facts.**

$$3 + 1 = 4 \qquad 4 + 5 = 9 \qquad 1 + 5 = 6$$

_____   _____   _____

_____   _____   _____

4 # Draw a line to match the object with the shape.

WORD NUMBERS – 100-199

1 **Draw a line to match the word number to the number.**

one hundred sixty	141
one hundred forty-one	185
one hundred eighty-five	160
one hundred twenty-two	170
one hundred seventy	122
one hundred fifty-six	138
one hundred thirty-eight	156

2 **Write the number.**

129 = _____ hundred _____ tens _____ ones

363 = _____ hundreds _____ tens _____ ones

941 = _____ hundreds _____ tens _____ one

502 = _____ hundreds _____ tens _____ ones

655 = _____ hundreds _____ tens _____ ones

3 Julia cut the pie into 8 pieces. Jared ate 2 pieces. Julia had how many pieces left?

____ - ____ = ____ _____

9

④ **Circle the object that has a different shape.**

⑤ **Write the number that comes between.**

121 ___ 123   184 ___ 186

153 ___ 155   167 ___ 169

132 ___ 134   179 ___ 181

MONEY

① Write the numbers in the blanks.

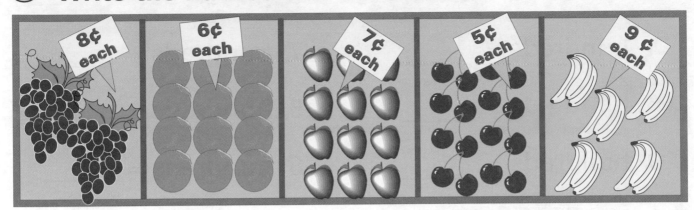

apple   ____¢   orange   ____¢   banana   ____¢
cherry +____¢   grape   +____¢   orange +____¢
total   ____¢   total   ____¢   total   ____¢

apple   ____¢   cherry   ____¢   grape   ____¢
grape   +____¢   banana +____¢   orange +____¢
total   ____¢   total   ____¢   total   ____¢

② Write the number that comes between.

126 ____ 128   158 ____ 160

135 ____ 137   172 ____ 174

104 ____ 106   143 ____ 145

③ **Write the numbers.**

1 hundred = _____   3 hundreds = _____

4 hundreds = _____   7 hundreds = _____

6 hundreds = _____   5 hundreds = _____

9 hundreds = _____   8 hundreds = _____

2 hundreds = _____

④ **Write the numbers.**

one hundred eighty-two   _____

one hundred twenty-six   _____

one hundred forty   _____

one hundred sixty-seven   _____

one hundred thirteen   _____

one hundred five   _____

⑤ Bert had 8 horses on his farm. His father sold 3 of them. Bert has how many horses left?

_____ - _____ = _____ _____

12

CALENDAR – DAYS OF THE WEEK

① **Write the missing numbers.**

January

Sunday	Monday	Tuesday	Wednesday	Thursday	Friday	Saturday
			1	**2**		
	6				**10**	
		14		**16**		
19					**24**	
	27				**31**	

② **Write the answers.**

What day is January 1? _____

What day is the last day of January? _____

What day is 2 days after January 15? _____

What day is 1 day before January 20? _____

③ Jill saw 6 birds on the bird bath. 4 more birds joined them. How many birds were on the bird bath?

④ Write the correct time.

:
_____

:
_____

:
_____

:
_____

⑤ Write the hundreds, tens, and ones. Write the number.

1 hundred 8 tens 5 ones =_____ + _____ + _____ = _____

3 hundreds 6 tens 3 ones =_____ + _____ + _____ = _____

7 hundreds 3 tens 8 ones =_____ + _____ + _____ = _____

5 hundreds 5 tens 4 ones =_____ + _____ + _____ = _____

⑥ Draw a line to match the word number to the number.

one hundred ninety-six	135
one hundred thirty-five	196
one hundred eighty-eight	150
one hundred seventy-three	173
one hundred fifty	149
one hundred forty-nine	188

14

BAR GRAPH

1 **Write the answers.**

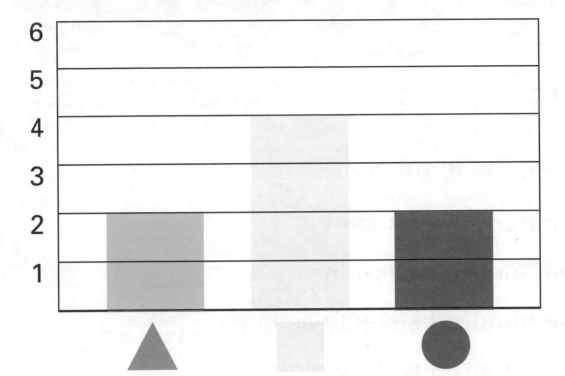

How many blue blocks above the triangle? _____

How many triangles are there? _____

How many yellow blocks above the square? _____

How many squares are there? _____

How many red blocks are above the circle? _____

How many circles are there? _____

2 **Write the numbers.**

385 = 300 + 80 + 5   742 = ____ + ____ + ____

521 = ____ + ____ + ____   690 = ____ + ____ + ____

3 **Draw the hands on the clocks.**

6:15   3:45   2:45   9:15

4 **Write the numbers.**

one hundred fifteen   _____

one hundred fifty-nine   _____

one hundred seventy-seven   _____

one hundred twenty-eight   _____

one hundred ninety-two   _____

one hundred thirty-one   _____

one hundred forty-five   _____

5 **Write the value of each set.**

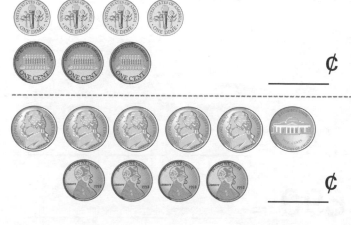

_____ ¢

_____ ¢

_____ ¢

_____ ¢

16

NUMBER ORDER –
< AND > OVER 100

1 Write < or > in the blanks.

| 137 ___ 140 | 154 ___ 151 |

163 ___ 136   195 ___ 159

| 183 ___ 181 | 168 ___ 175 |

2 Color the blocks for the bar graph.

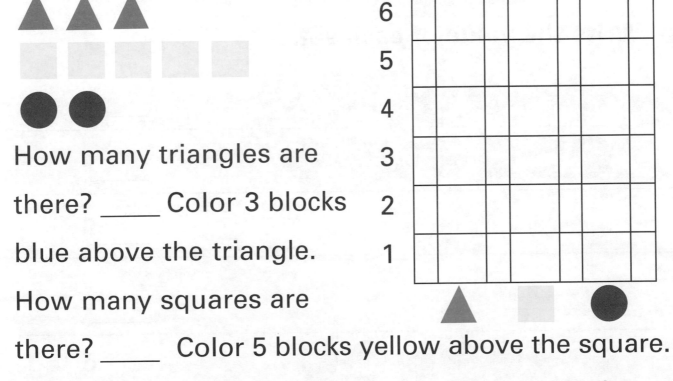

How many triangles are there? ____ Color 3 blocks blue above the triangle.

How many squares are there? ____ Color 5 blocks yellow above the square.

How many circles are there? ____ Color 2 blocks red above the circle.

17

③ **Write the numbers.**

300 + 60 + 5 = ____

500 + 70 + 3 = ____

800 + 50 + 9 = ____

200 + 40 + 7 = ____

900 + 80 + 2 = ____

100 + 30 + 4 = ____

④ **Write the value of each set.**

 ____ ¢

 ____ ¢

 ____ ¢

 ____ ¢

 ____ ¢

 ____ ¢

MONEY – DOLLAR

Front   Back

$1.00   one dollar   100¢

$ This sign means dollars.

(.) A point is used to separate the dollars and cents.

① **Count the dollars.**

   $ ____.00

  $ ____.00

 $ ____.00

② Henry had 8 balloons for his birthday. 5 of the
balloons broke during his party. How many
balloons did he have left when the party was over?

    ____ - ____ = ____ _____

19

3 **Color the blocks on the bar graph.**

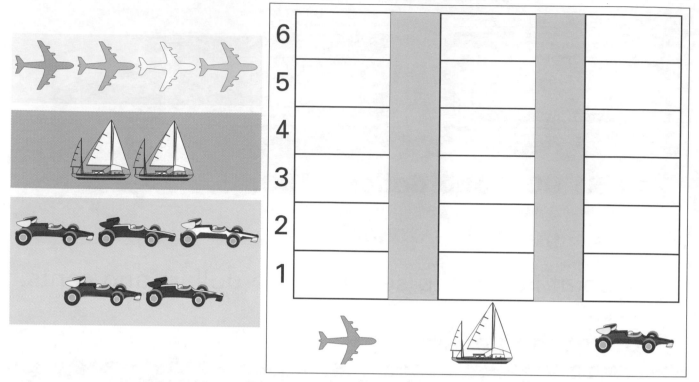

Color a block on the graph for each airplane.

Color a block on the graph for each ship.

Color a block on the graph for each car.

4 **Write the correct time.**

_____ : _____   _____ : _____   _____ : _____   _____ : _____

5 There were 8 boys and 8 girls at Jackie's party. How many children were at Jackie's party?

TEST 9

1 **Write the correct time.** 8 pts. total for this exercise.

:　　　　　　:　　　　　　:　　　　　　:

:　　　　　　:　　　　　　:　　　　　　:

2 **Write the fractional part that is shaded.** 8 pts.

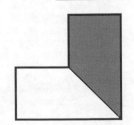 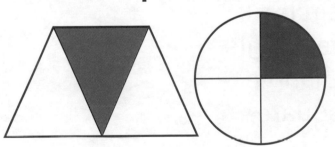 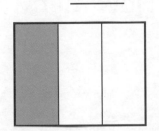 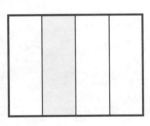 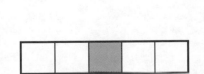 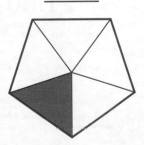

③ **Write the numbers.** 9 pts. total for this exercise.

483 has a _____ in the ones' place.

297 has a _____ in the tens' place.

165 has a _____ in the hundreds' place.

340 has a _____ in the tens' place.

628 has a _____ in the ones' place.

512 has a _____ in the tens' place.

734 has a _____ in the hundreds' place.

856 has a _____ in the ones' place.

971 has a _____ in the hundreds' place.

④ **Draw a line to match a shape to its name.** 4 pts.

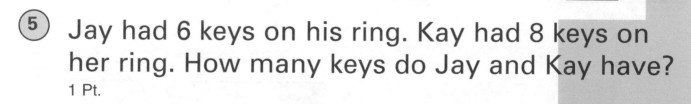

circle
rectangle
triangle
square

⑤ Jay had 6 keys on his ring. Kay had 8 keys on her ring. How many keys do Jay and Kay have?
1 Pt.

____ + ____ = ____ _____

22   30 pts. Total

SHOW YOUR SKILLS

① **Draw the hour (short) hand on the clocks.**

10:30   8:15   4:45   6:00

11:15   7:00   1:30   3:45

② **Subtract.**

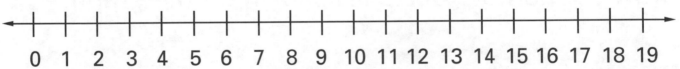

13	11	10	12	11	14
- 4	- 6	- 8	- 9	- 4	- 5

15	10	13	14	15	12
- 7	- 6	- 7	- 8	- 6	- 3

23

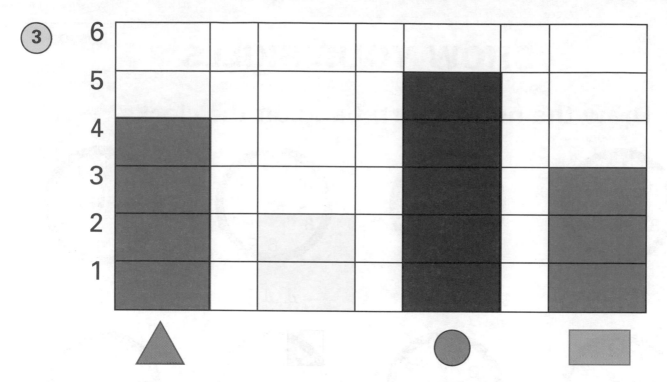

Draw the number of triangles shown on the graph.

Draw the number of squares shown on the graph.

Draw the number of circles shown on the graph.

Draw the number of rectangles shown on the graph.

④ **Write < or > between each set.**

138 ___ 142   141 ___ 114

175 ___ 184   108 ___ 111

156 ___ 123   160 ___ 197

CENTIMETERS

① **Write the numbers.**

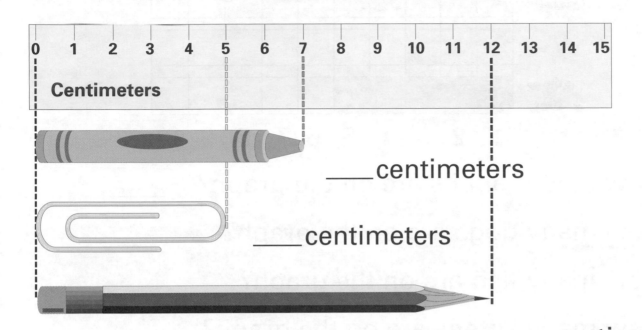

_____centimeters

_____centimeters

_____centimeters

② **Draw both hands on the clocks.**

4:15　　　　8:30　　　　10:00　　　　12:45

2:00　　　　11:30　　　　9:15　　　　6:45

25

③ Write the number.

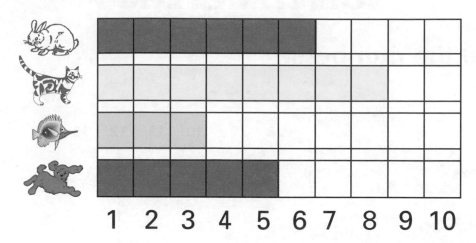

How many rabbits are on the graph?   _____

How many dogs are on the graph?   _____

How many fish are on the graph?   _____

How many kittens are on the graph?   _____

④ 8 cows were in the barnyard. 5 cows then went into the barn. How many cows were left in the yard?

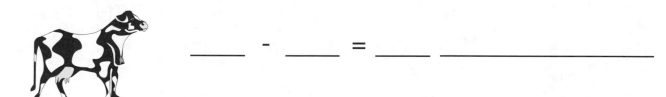

_____ - _____ = _____ _____

Sue picked 7 flowers in the woods. Mae picked 5 flowers. How many flowers did they pick?

ADDITION – THREE
DOUBLE DIGIT NUMBERS

1 **Write the answers.**

$$\begin{array}{r} 53 \\ 31 \\ +12 \\ \hline \end{array}\quad \begin{array}{r} 21 \\ 22 \\ +53 \\ \hline \end{array}\quad \begin{array}{r} 41 \\ 16 \\ +32 \\ \hline \end{array}\quad \begin{array}{r} 34 \\ 12 \\ +23 \\ \hline \end{array}\quad \begin{array}{r} 24 \\ 23 \\ +12 \\ \hline \end{array}\quad \begin{array}{r} 20 \\ 45 \\ +13 \\ \hline \end{array}$$

$$\begin{array}{r} 12 \\ 11 \\ +54 \\ \hline \end{array}\quad \begin{array}{r} 34 \\ 12 \\ +42 \\ \hline \end{array}\quad \begin{array}{r} 52 \\ 32 \\ +11 \\ \hline \end{array}\quad \begin{array}{r} 54 \\ 32 \\ +10 \\ \hline \end{array}\quad \begin{array}{r} 14 \\ 21 \\ +53 \\ \hline \end{array}\quad \begin{array}{r} 21 \\ 36 \\ +12 \\ \hline \end{array}$$

2 **Write the letters in the blanks.**

___ ___ ___   ___   ___ ___ ___ ___

fourth	W	sixth	S	third	O
seventh	F	second	N	fifth	I
first	S	ninth	N	eighth	U

③ Write the number.

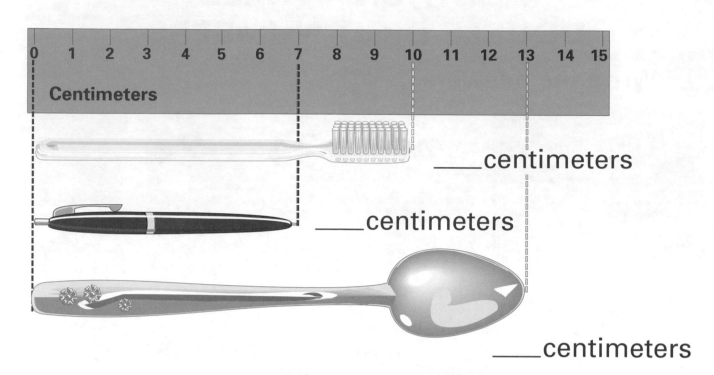

_____ centimeters

_____ centimeters

_____ centimeters

④ Subtract.

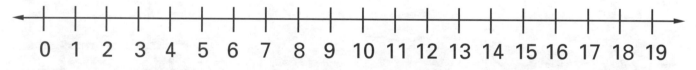

14	11	13	12	10	11
- 7	- 2	- 8	- 7	- 1	- 4

12	15	14	13	10	16
- 5	- 7	- 5	- 4	- 6	- 8

28

SHAPES

1

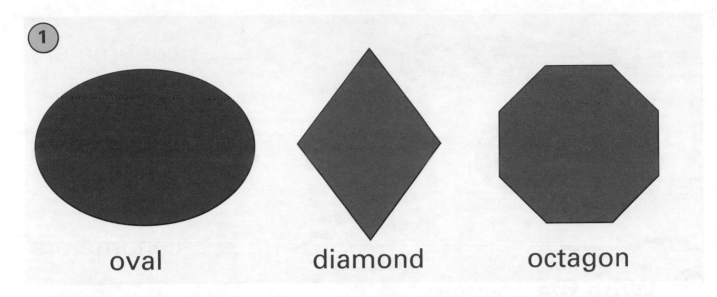

oval   diamond   octagon

Color the oval purple. Color the diamond orange. Color the octagon brown.

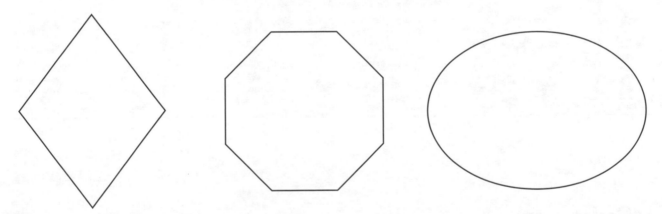

2 **Write the number that comes after.**

126 ____   131 ____   157 ____

185 ____   104 ____   193 ____

172 ____   118 ____   149 ____

③ **Measure the objects.**

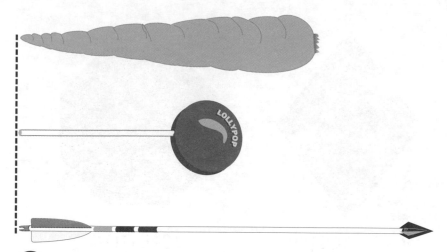

_____ centimeters

_____ centimeters

_____ centimeters

④ **Write the answers.**

13	23	24	65	14	27
21	31	22	10	11	20
+32	+45	+43	+13	+12	+52

⑤ **Subtract.**

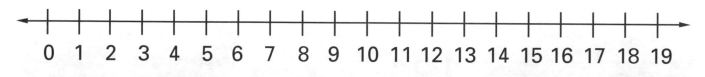

0 1 2 3 4 5 6 7 8 9 10 11 12 13 14 15 16 17 18 19

10	14	15	12	11	10
- 9	- 5	- 8	- 6	- 9	- 5

ODD NUMBERS

① **Write the missing odd numbers.**

1　3　___　___　9　___　___

15　___　___　21　___　___　___

29　___　___　___　37　___　___

43　___　___　49　___　___　___

② **Draw a line to match the object to the shape.**

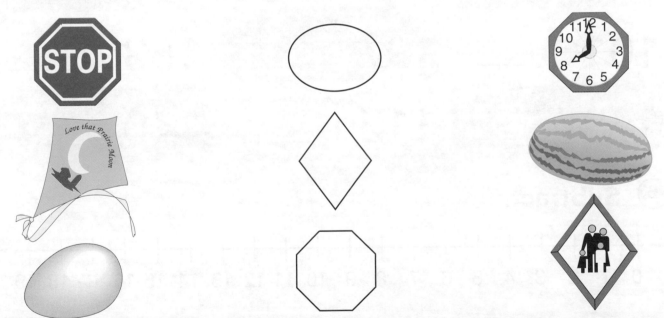

③ Jack had 12 baseball cards. He gave 4 of them to Joe. How many baseball cards did Jack have left?

___ - ___ = ___ _____

31

④ **Measure the lines with a centimeter ruler. Write the answers.**

_____ centimeters

_____ centimeters

_____ centimeters

⑤ **Write the number that comes after.**

186 _____   125 _____   134 _____

101 _____   197 _____   153 _____

178 _____   112 _____   140 _____

⑥ **Subtract.**

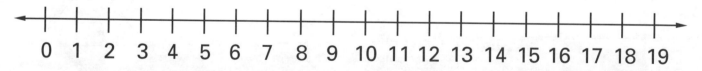

0	1	2	3	4	5	6	7	8	9	10	11	12	13	14	15	16	17	18	19

$$\begin{array}{r} 11 \\ -\ 5 \\ \hline \end{array}\qquad \begin{array}{r} 15 \\ -\ 7 \\ \hline \end{array}\qquad \begin{array}{r} 13 \\ -\ 4 \\ \hline \end{array}\qquad \begin{array}{r} 12 \\ -\ 8 \\ \hline \end{array}\qquad \begin{array}{r} 14 \\ -\ 7 \\ \hline \end{array}\qquad \begin{array}{r} 11 \\ -\ 2 \\ \hline \end{array}$$

SEQUENCE OF EVENTS

1 John just got out of bed.

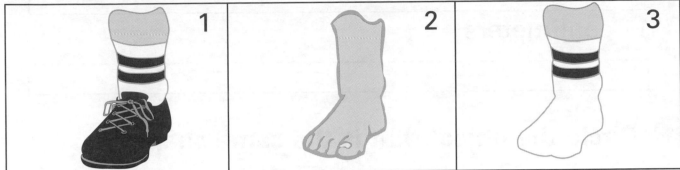

Which comes first?   1   2   3

Which comes last?   1   2   3

Making a snow man.

Which comes first?   1   2   3

Which comes last?   1   2   3

2 Write the number that comes after.

108 ____   192 ____   150 ____

171 ____   117 ____   143 ____

3 **Draw a line with the ruler.**

4 centimeters

•

11 centimeters

•

4 **Circle the object that is the same shape.**

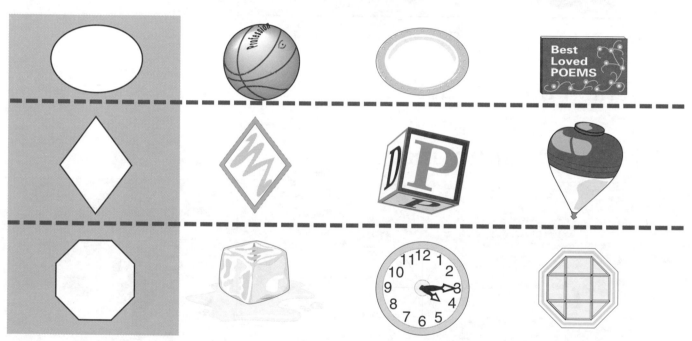

5 **Color the squares blue that have odd numbers.**

2	1	8	11	13	15	4	31	33	35	10
6	3	12	14	16	17	18	37	20	22	24
30	5	32	34	21	19	36	39	41	43	38
44	7	46	48	50	23	52	54	56	45	58
64	9	66	29	27	25	68	51	49	47	70

PLACE VALUE – ONE HUNDREDS

1 **Write the answers.**

458 = ___ + ___ + ___

369 = ___ + ___ + ___

217 = ___ + ___ + ___

764 = ___ + ___ + ___

300 + 60 + 5 = ___

500 + 70 + 3 = ___

800 + 50 + 9 = ___

600 + 30 + 2 = ___

2 **Write the number that comes before.**

___ 181   ___ 106   ___ 127

___ 195   ___ 133   ___ 154

___ 172   ___ 110   ___ 148

35

3 Mother is making cookies.

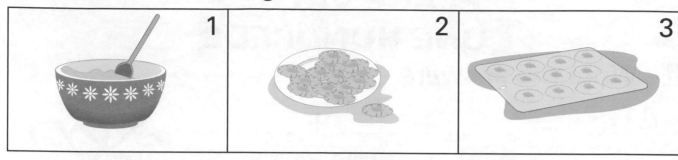

Which picture comes first?   1   2   3

Which picture comes last?   1   2   3

Jack planted a tree.

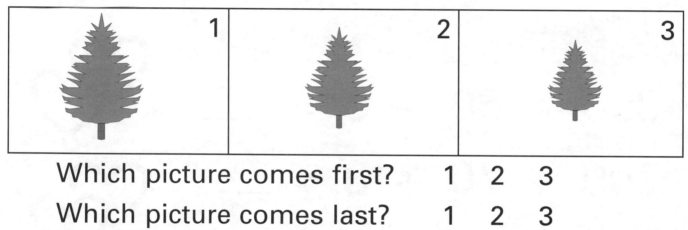

Which picture comes first?   1   2   3

Which picture comes last?   1   2   3

4 **Write the missing even numbers.**

130 132 ____ ____ 138 ____

142 ____ ____ 148 ____ ____

154 ____ ____ ____ 162 ____

166 ____ 170 ____ ____

MEASUREMENT – LIQUID

1

ounce   cup   pint   quart   gallon

2 **Write the answers.**

390 = ___ + ___ + ___

428 = ___ + ___ + ___

746 = ___ + ___ + ___

274 = ___ + ___ + ___

3 **Write the number that comes before.**

___ 182   ___ 100   ___ 128

___ 191   ___ 136   ___ 157

___ 175   ___ 113   ___ 144

(4) Circle the correct word.

183	even	odd		127	even	odd
25	even	odd		64	even	odd
76	even	odd		30	even	odd

(5) Father is getting ready for work.

Which picture comes first?   1   2   3

Which picture comes last?   1   2   3

(6) Subtract.

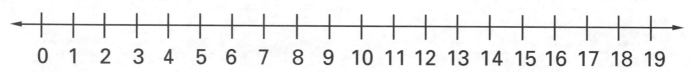

```
  15      13      18      14      16      12
-  6    -  5    -  9    -  8    -  7    -  5
```

```
  11      17      10      11      10      15
-  4    -  8    -  1    -  8    -  4    -  9
```

38

NUMBER SEQUENCE

1 **Circle every third number after 2.**

(2) 3 4 5 6 7 8 9 10

11 12 13 14 15 16 17 18 19

20 21 22 23 24 25 26 27 28

Write the circled numbers on the blanks.

_____ _____ _____ _____ _____ _____ _____ _____

2 **Draw a line to match the container to its name.**

pint   ounce   quart   gallon   cup

3 **Write = or ≠ between each set.**

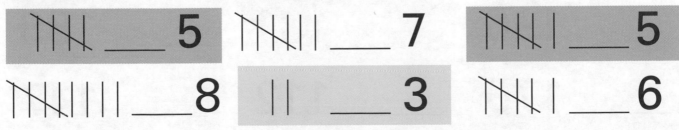

IIII \ ___ 5   IIII \ III ___ 7   IIII \ I ___ 5

IIII \ IIII ___ 8   II ___ 3   IIII \ I ___ 6

39

④ Circle the pennies.

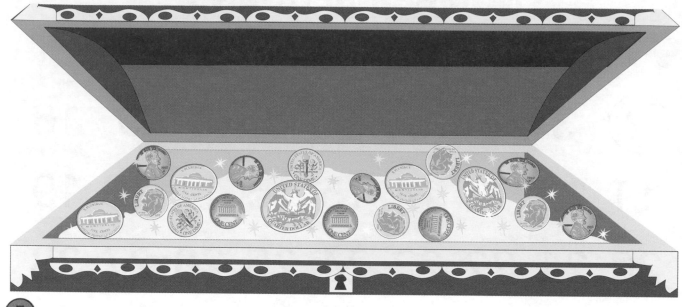

⑤ Jane is going shopping.

Which picture comes first?   1   2   3

Which picture comes last?   1   2   3

⑥ Write the number that comes before.

____ 183   ____ 105   ____ 124

____ 196   ____ 131   ____ 158

____ 170   ____ 112   ____ 147

ESTIMATION

① **Write the answers.**

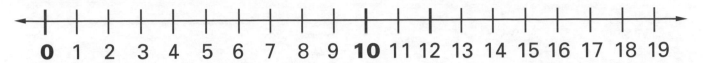

0 1 2 3 4 5 6 7 8 9 **10** 11 12 13 14 15 16 17 18 19

Is 3 closer to 0 or 10? _____

Is 7 closer to 0 or 10? _____

Is 9 closer to 0 or 10 ? _____

Is 2 closer to 0 or 10 ? _____

Is 4 closer to 0 or 10? _____

② **Write the next 3 numbers.**

5　8　11　☐　☐　☐

7　10　13　☐　☐　☐

③ There were 12 cookies on the plate. Sue and Jan ate 4 of them. How many cookies were left on the plate?

____ - ____ = ____ _____

41

④ Write the name.

_____

_____

_____

_____

_____

⑤ Circle the dimes.

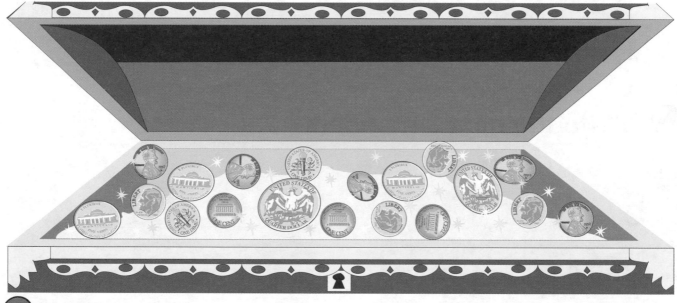

⑥ Write = or ≠ between each set. Read the set.

6+4 ___ 10	3+9 ___ 12	7+2 ___ 10
5+1 ___ 6	8+5 ___ 12	6+0 ___ 7
4+5 ___ 8	6+5 ___ 14	7+2 ___ 11

42

7 **Write the answers.**

```
  1        5        2        3        4        6
  8        1        7        2        1        2
 +2       +5       +6       +3       +7       +7
```

```
  3        6        4        5        1        4
  5        3        3        2        6        4
 +5       +2       +3       +3       +7       +4
```

```
 27       73       34       52       31       60
+41      +21      +15      +46      +24      +16
```

```
 31       41       20       12       30       11
 12       23       14       46       35       45
+26      +33      +64      +21      +13      +32
```

8 Write the answers.

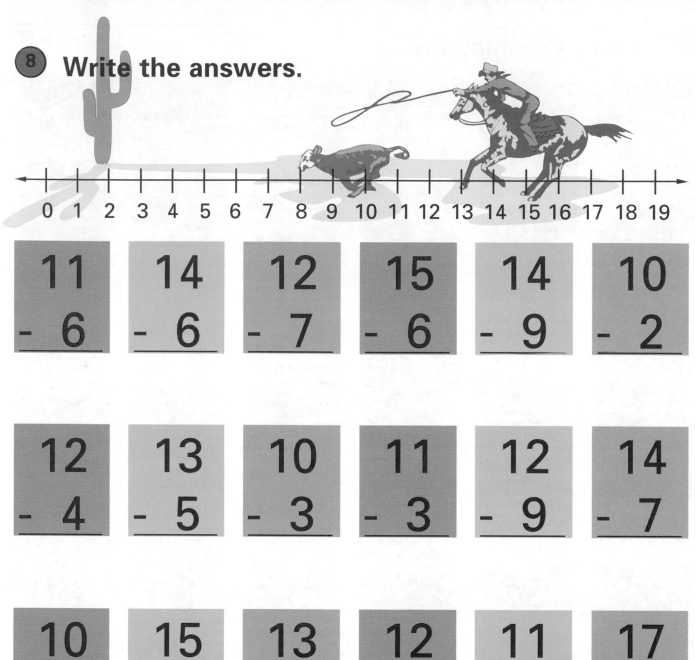

11 − 6	14 − 6	12 − 7	15 − 6	14 − 9	10 − 2
12 − 4	13 − 5	10 − 3	11 − 3	12 − 9	14 − 7
10 − 6	15 − 8	13 − 8	12 − 6	11 − 7	17 − 9
16 − 9	16 − 8	11 − 9	13 − 7	10 − 8	12 − 8

TEST 10

① 3 pts. for this exercise.

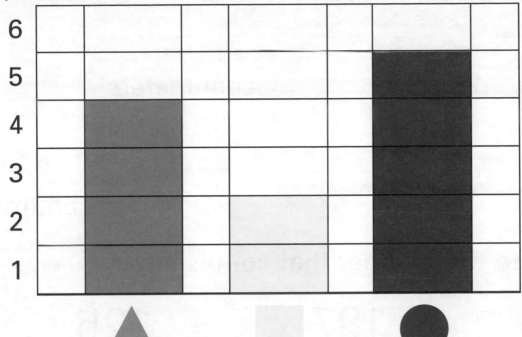

How many s on the bar graph? ____

How many s on the bar graph? ____

How many s on the bar graph? ____

② **Draw a line to match the shape to its name.** 3 pts.

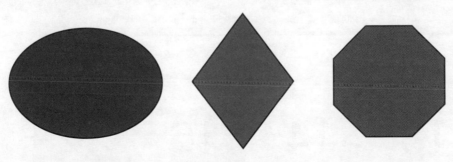

octagon   oval   diamond

③ **Measure the lines with the centimeter ruler. Write the answer.** 3 pts. for this exercise.

_____ centimeters

_____ centimeters

_____ centimeters

④ **Write the number that comes after.** 3 pts. for this exercise.

163 ___   187 ___   125 ___

⑤ **Subtract.** 12 pts. for this exercise.

```
<---+---+---+---+---+---+---+---+---+---+---+---+---+---+---+---+---+---+---+--->
    0   1   2   3   4   5   6   7   8   9  10  11  12  13  14  15  16  17  18  19
```

15	12	11	13	11	10
- 6	- 7	- 3	- 8	- 5	- 4

14	18	14	16	12	17
- 9	- 9	- 7	- 7	- 3	- 8

46

24 pts. Total

ADDITION – TWO
TRIPLE DIGIT NUMBERS

① **Write the answers.**

```
  153      261      427      523      214
+234     +405     +151     +246     +733
```

```
  350      627      462      162      124
+413     +351     +123     +532     +124
```

② **Write the numbers.**

one hundred eighty-three _____

one hundred fifty-one _____

one hundred fourteen _____

③ **Write the correct time.**

___ : ___   ___ : ___   ___ : ___   ___ : ___

47

4 **Circle the nickels.**

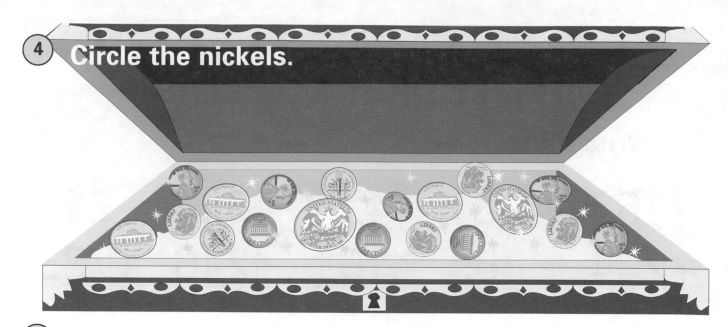

5 **Circle the object that is about 10 inches tall.**

6 **Circle every fourth number after 3.**

(3) 4 5 6 7 8 9 10 11

12 13 14 15 16 17 18 19 20

21 22 23 24 25 26 27 28 29

Write the circled numbers on the blanks.

☐ ☐ ☐ ☐ ☐ ☐ ☐

BAR GRAPH

1

6						
5						
4						
3						
2						
1						

How many sleds are on the bar graph? _____

How many skis are on the bar graph? _____

How many ice skates are on the bar graph? _____

2 **Write the numbers.**

one hundred thirty _____

one hundred forty-seven _____

one hundred eighteen _____

3 **Write the next 3 numbers.**

5 7 9 ___ ___ ___

41 43 45 ___ ___ ___

49

4 ## Circle "about" how many fish there are.

15

4

40

5 ## Write the correct time.

| : | : | : | : |

| : | : | : | : |

6 ## Circle the quarters.

50

WORD PROBLEMS – SUBTRACTION

① John has 5 matchbox cars. Kyle has 3 matchbox cars. John has how many more cars than Kyle?

____ - ____ = ____ _____

Mary ate 8 marshmallows. Sally ate 5 marshmallows. Mary ate how many more marshmallows than Sally?

____ - ____ = ____ _____

There were 9 ducks and 6 swans on the pond. How many more ducks were there than swans?

____ - ____ = ____ _____

② **Circle every sixth number after 3. Write the circled numbers on the blanks.**

③ 4 5 6 7 8 9 10 11

12 13 14 15 16 17 18 19 20

21 22 23 24 25 26 27 28 29

☐ ☐ ☐ ☐ ☐

③ **Write the subtraction facts.**

6+2=8   2+4=6   1+5=6

_____   _____   _____

_____   _____   _____

④ **Circle the object that is about 30 inches long.**

⑤ **Circle the numbers greater than 150.**

168   127   146   172   115

130   151   180   108   197

159   173   112   164   146

⑥ **Write the correct time.**

___ : ___   ___ : ___   ___ : ___   ___ : ___

⑦ Color the blocks on the bar graph.

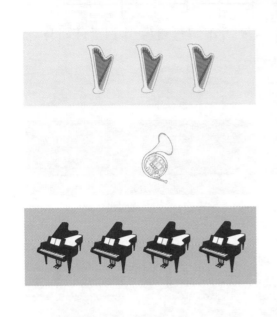

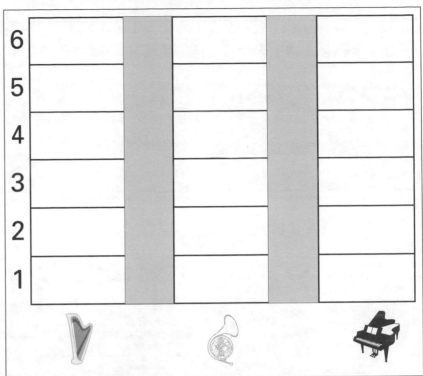

Color a block on the graph for each harp.

Color a block on the graph for each french horn.

Color a block on the graph for each piano.

⑧ Add.

112 +131	214 +251	142 +603	536 +233	234 +512

214 +584	325 +161	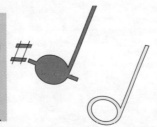	243 +722	496 +302

53

⑨ Subtract.

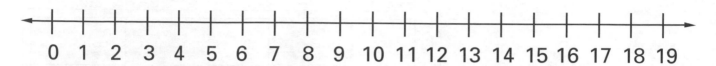

0 1 2 3 4 5 6 7 8 9 10 11 12 13 14 15 16 17 18 19

| 13
− 8 | 11
− 3 | 15
− 6 | 10
− 3 | 12
− 9 | 14
− 5 |

| 12
− 8 | 13
− 6 | 17
− 8 | 11
− 7 | 10
− 4 | 11
− 2 |

| 10
− 6 | 11
− 4 | 15
− 8 | 18
− 9 | 13
− 5 | 12
− 7 |

| 12
− 5 | 16
− 7 | 13
− 4 | 14
− 9 | 11
− 6 | 10
− 7 |

54

MONEY

1 **Draw a line to match each coin to its value.**

5¢

1¢

$1.00

25¢

10¢

5¢

1¢

10¢

$1.00

25¢

2 **Circle the numbers less than 150.**

147	165	113	174	160
131	181	109	152	198
146	128	169	173	116

3 Susie has 7 people in her family. Jane has 4 people in her family. Susie has how many more people in her family than Jane?

_____ - _____ = _____ _____

55

(4)

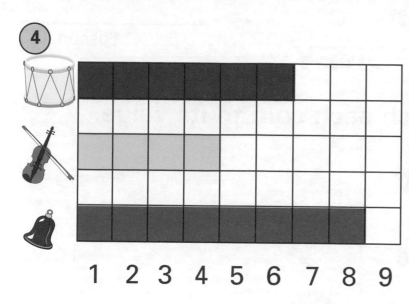

How many drums are on the bar graph?_____

How many violins are on the bar graph?____

How many bells are on the bar graph?____

1 2 3 4 5 6 7 8 9

(5) **Write the subtraction facts.**

$$3+5=8 \qquad 2+1=3 \qquad 4+3=7$$

_____ _____ _____

_____ _____ _____

(6) **Write the correct time.**

__:__ _____ __:__ _____ __:__ _____ __:__ _____

DOZEN

1 **Color a dozen objects in each set.**

2 **Write the value of each set of money.**

_____ ¢

_____ ¢

_____ ¢

$ _____ . _____

3 **Write the subtraction facts.**

5+7=12	3+8=11	6+9=15

④ **Draw a line to match the shape to its name.**

oval

rectangle

square

diamond

circle

octagon

triangle

⑤ **Add.**

242	623	473	726	134
+115	+126	+221	+172	+424

124	331	416	521	832
+735	+535	+333	+242	+146

152	275		100	531
+830	+304		+568	+104

NUMBER ORDER – BEFORE AND AFTER OVER 100

① **Write the number that comes before and after.**

_____ 136 _____   _____ 172 _____

_____ 150 _____   _____ 127 _____

_____ 191 _____   _____ 149 _____

_____ 108 _____   _____ 183 _____

② **Write the name of each shape.**

square   rectangle   circle   triangle
oval   diamond   octagon

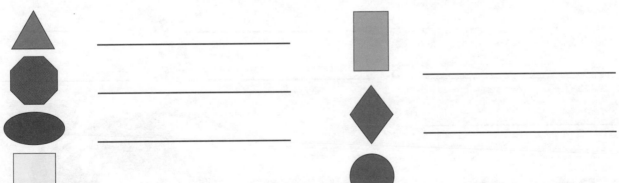

_____   _____

_____   _____

_____   _____

③ **Add.**

325	123	732	508
+410	+345	+163	+341

59

④ **Measure each object. Write the number.**

_____ centimeters

_____ centimeters

_____ centimeters

⑤ **Write the days of the week in order.**

Monday   Wednesday   Saturday   Friday

Tuesday   Sunday   Thursday

1. _____   2. _____   3. _____

4. _____   5. _____   6. _____

7. _____

⑥ **Draw a dozen triangles.**

60

SUBTRACTION – WITHOUT NUMBER LINE

1 **Subtract.**

12	5	15	2	13	3
- 6	- 4	- 7	- 1	- 9	- 3

6	10	14	9	11	4
- 1	- 5	- 6	- 3	- 8	- 4

10	8	16	9	17	7
- 1	- 7	- 8	- 0	- 9	- 5

2 **Draw the outlines of the shapes.**

square   triangle   rectangle   circle

octagon   oval   diamond

③ **Measure the lines with a centimeter ruler. Write the answers.**

_____ centimeters

_____ centimeters

_____ centimeters

④ **Add.**

482	372	164	153	150
+515	+322	+832	+546	+229

758	405	623	643	321
+140	+461	+270	+210	+248

⑤ **Write the number that comes before and after.**

____ 131 ____   ____ 179 ____

____ 157 ____   ____ 120 ____

____ 196 ____   ____ 142 ____

ODD NUMBERS

1 **Dot to dot using odd numbers.**

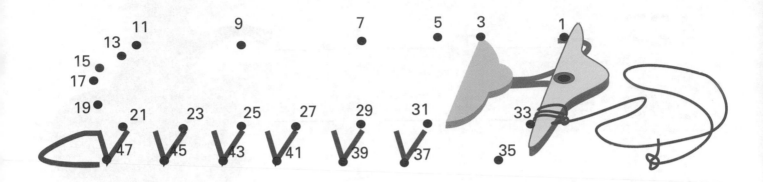

11 9 7 5 3 1
13
15
17
19 21 23 25 27 29 31 33
47 45 43 41 39 37 35

2 **Number the pictures in the correct order.**
Joe is building a dog house.

_____   _____   _____

3 **Write the number that comes before and after.**

____ 139 ____   ____ 171 ____

____ 153 ____   ____ 115 ____

____ 192 ____   ____ 146 ____

63

④ **Write the answers.**

156 = ___ + ___ + ___

427 = ___ + ___ + ___

389 = ___ + ___ + ___

734 = ___ + ___ + ___

265 = ___ + ___ + ___

⑤ **Draw a line with the centimeter ruler.**

7 centimeters

•

11 centimeters

•

4 centimeters

•

⑥ **Subtract.**

12	5	15	2	13	3
- 6	- 4	- 7	- 1	- 9	- 3

64

SOLIDS

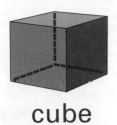
cube

sphere

cylinder

cone

① Color the sphere yellow.
Color the cylinder green.
Color the cube red.
Color the cone blue.

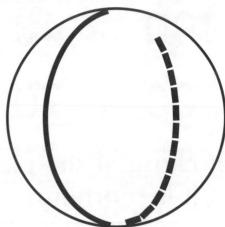

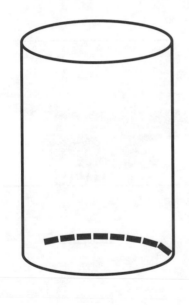

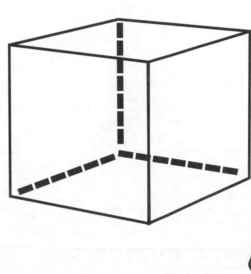

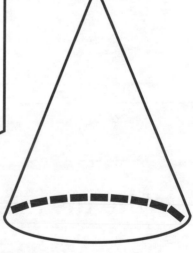

② Jonathan had 12 chicks. James had 7 chicks.
Jonathan had how many more chicks than
James had?

_____ - _____ = _____ _____

3 **Write the answers.**

600 + 50 + 4 = _____

700 + 30 + 8 = _____

100 + 40 + 9 = _____

500 + 70 + 1 = _____

4 **Number the pictures in the correct order.**
It is morning.

noon   morning   evening

_____   _____   _____

5 **Write the missing numbers.**

101 103 105 ___ ___ 111

113 ___ 117 ___ 121 ___

___ 127 ___ 131 ___ 135

SHOW YOUR SKILLS

1 **Write the numbers.**

367 has a _____ in the ones' place.

637 has a _____ in the tens' place.

763 has a _____ in the hundreds' place.

736 has a _____ in the tens' place.

673 has a _____ in the hundreds' place.

376 has a _____ in the ones' place.

2 **Draw a line to match the solid to its name.**

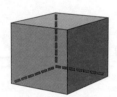   

sphere   cone   cube   cylinder

3 **Write = or ≠ between each set.**

14-6 ___ 8   12-8 ___ 5   11-5 ___ 6

10-4 ___ 5   13-7 ___ 6   16-9 ___ 7

67

4 Add.

5	7	3	9	6	8
+8	+5	+7	+2	+4	+6

16	24	38	15	72	46
+23	+53	+60	+11	+26	+41

5 Subtract.

3	10	18	4	14	5
- 2	- 6	- 9	- 4	- 8	- 2

11	6	14	12	7	15
- 7	- 4	- 6	- 5	- 4	- 9

15	12	13	8	16	11
- 6	- 3	- 4	- 6	- 7	- 9

TEST 11

1 **A baby is born.** 2 pts. for this exercise.

What picture comes first?   1   2   3

What picture comes last?   1   2   3

2 **Write the answers.** 4 pts. for this exercise.

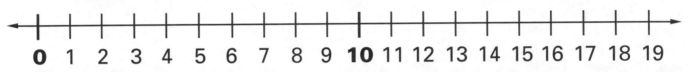

0 1 2 3 4 5 6 7 8 9 **10** 11 12 13 14 15 16 17 18 19

Is 7 closer to 0 or 10?   _____

Is 3 closer to 0 or 10?   _____

Is 4 closer to 0 or 10 ?   _____

Is 9 closer to 0 or 10 ?   _____

3 **Write the value for each set of coins.** 2 pts.

_____ ¢

_____ ¢

4 Add. 11 pts.

5	6	5	3	4	6
4	2	1	2	3	3
+6	+3	+8	+9	+7	+4

124	321	243	517	163
+134	+362	+750	+241	+504

5 Subtract. 12 pts.

0 1 2 3 4 5 6 7 8 9 10 11 12 13 14 15 16 17 18 19

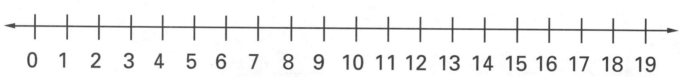

11	13	8	10	14	15
- 6	- 7	- 5	- 2	- 5	- 8

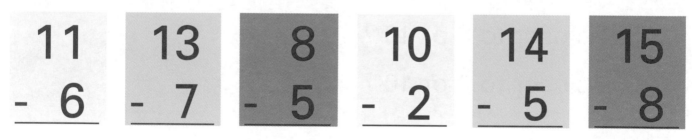

12	14	11	9	10	13
- 8	- 6	- 3	- 3	- 7	- 5

31 pts. Total

WORD NUMBERS 100-199

1 **Write = or ≠ between each set.**

one hundred sixty-two _____ 126

one hundred eighty-five _____ 185

one hundred thirty _____ 103

one hundred thirteen _____ 113

one hundred fifty-eight _____ 158

one hundred forty-three _____ 134

2 **Write cone, cube, sphere, or cylinder on the lines.**

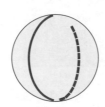 

_____   _____   _____   _____

3 Paul gave his dog 13 dog biscuits. The dog ate 7 of them. How many dog biscuits were left?

71

4 Add.

4 +7	3 +9	6 +8	8 +4	9 +6	7 +7

332 + 54	321 +374	340 +217	134 +702	254 +720

5 Subtract.

10 - 8	8 - 5	14 - 7	11 - 5	10 - 2	12 - 6

13 - 9	12 - 3	15 - 7	6 - 4	11 - 3	9 - 6

6 Joan ate 3 scoops of ice cream. Bill ate 5 scoops. They ate how many scoops of ice cream altogether?

72

ADDITION

① Add.

3	3	5	7	32	14
6	5	2	1	13	61
+4	+5	+6	+7	+23	+23

13	21	84	17	61	65
+ 3	+31	+12	+22	+13	+31

211	328	253	243	147
+486	+170	+632	+554	+740

② Write the numbers.

one hundred twenty-three   _____

one hundred forty-seven   _____

one hundred ninety-five   _____

one hundred eighteen   _____

73

3 Draw a line to match the solid with the picture.

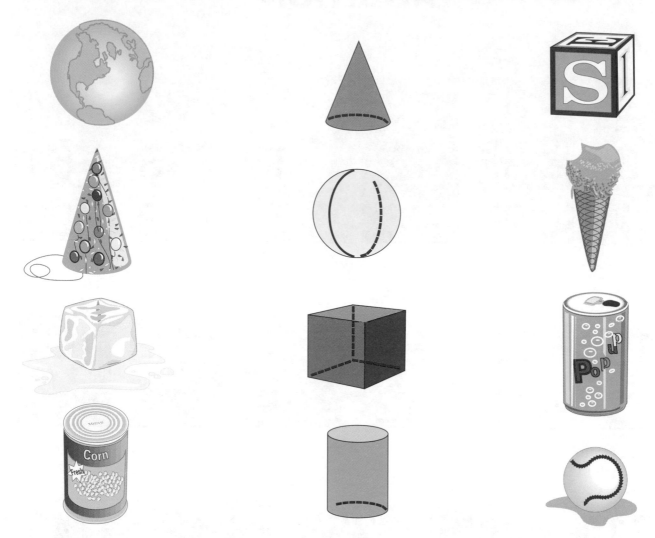

4 Mike gathered 5 eggs from one nest in the chicken house and 7 from another nest. Mike gathered how many eggs?

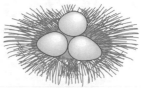

There were 13 cars and 6 trucks in the parking lot. How many more cars were there than trucks?

74

ESTIMATION

(1) Write the answers.

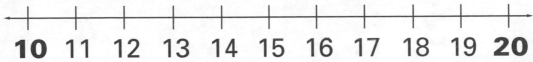

```
10  11  12  13  14  15  16  17  18  19  20
```

Is 11 closer to 10 or 20? _____

Is 16 closer to 10 or 20? _____

Is 18 closer to 10 or 20? _____

Is 13 closer to 10 or 20? _____

Is 17 closer to 10 or 20? _____

(2) Draw a line to match the solid to its name.

   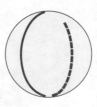

cone   cylinder   sphere   cube

(3) Write the numbers.

one hundred fifty-one _____

one hundred eighty _____

one hundred thirty-two _____

4 Add.

4	6	3	6	5	2
3	3	2	1	4	2
+3	+4	+6	+8	+7	+9

213	345	415	362	173
+714	+134	+121	+325	+312

5 Subtract.

13	12	16	11	16	8
- 6	- 6	- 9	- 2	- 8	- 2

12	17	10	13	12	10
- 8	- 8	- 7	- 8	- 7	- 2

BAR GRAPH

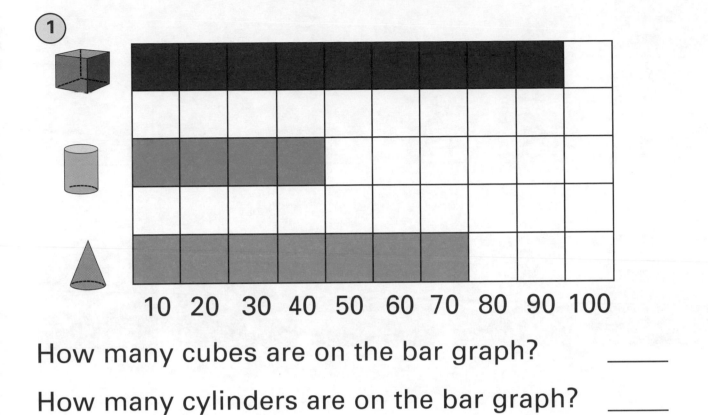

10 20 30 40 50 60 70 80 90 100

How many cubes are on the bar graph? _____

How many cylinders are on the bar graph? _____

How many cones are on the bar graph? _____

② **Measure the line with a centimeter ruler. Circle the correct answer.**

about **7** or **8** centimeters

about **10** or **11** centimeters

about **7** or **8** centimeters

77

③ **Add.**

4	4	7	3	2	6
4	2	2	3	3	3
+3	+6	+5	+9	+7	+8

321	813	249	102	621
+504	+156	+150	+662	+147

④ **Subtract.**

13	10	11	9	8	7
- 5	- 3	- 6	- 9	- 5	- 5

8	10	7	12	9	14
- 1	- 9	- 6	- 9	- 7	- 9

78

NUMBER ORDER – ORDINAL NUMBERS

① Write the letters in the blanks.

fourth	A	tenth	N	fifth	L
eleventh	E	sixth	E	eighth	T
ninth	I	second	Y	third	V
seventh	N	first	M		

② Write < or > between each set.

156 ___ 124   173 ___ 147

108 ___ 111   135 ___ 162

189 ___ 190   140 ___ 129

③ Sherry found 7 seashells on the beach. Ruth found 16 seashells. Ruth found how many more seashells than Sherry?

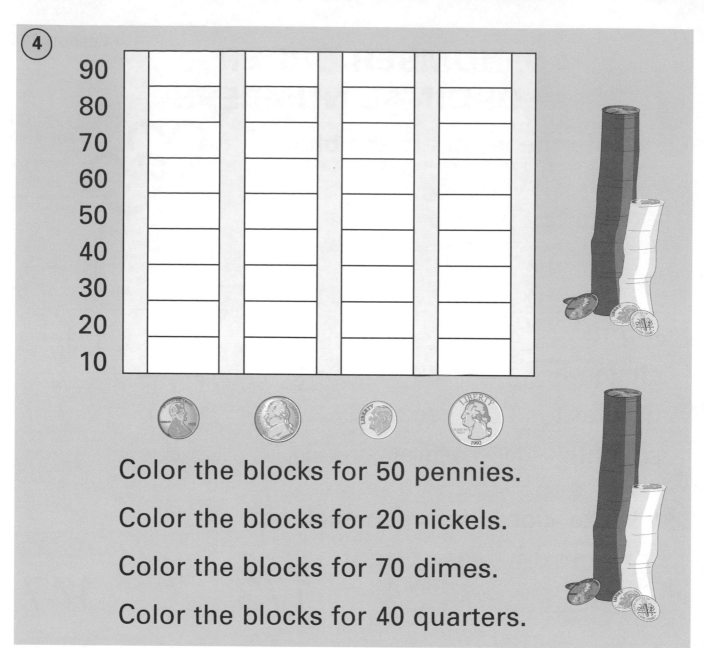

4

Color the blocks for 50 pennies.

Color the blocks for 20 nickels.

Color the blocks for 70 dimes.

Color the blocks for 40 quarters.

5 **Measure the objects with a centimeter ruler. Circle the correct answer.**

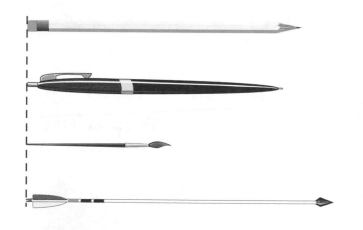

about **7** or **8** centimeters

about **6** or **7** centimeters

about **3** or **4** centimeters

about **8** or **9** centimeters

SHAPES

1 Color the circle red.

Color the rectangle green.

Color the square yellow.

Color the triangle blue.

Color the octagon brown.

Color the diamond orange.

Color the oval purple.

2 **Write the subtraction facts.**

6+3=9

7+8=15

4+8=12

_____

_____

_____

_____

_____

_____

5+9=14

9+2=11

4+1=5

_____

_____

_____

_____

_____

_____

③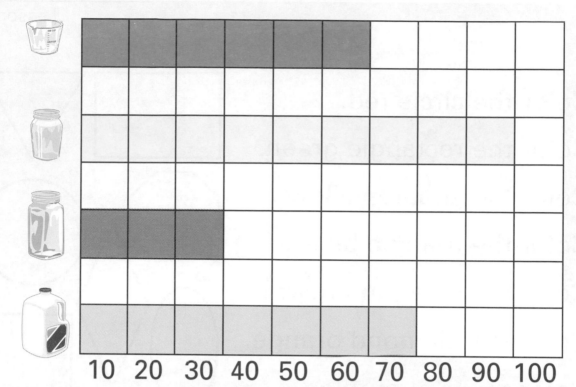

10   20   30   40   50   60   70   80   90   100

How many pints are on the bar graph? ____

How many gallons are on the bar graph? ____

How many cups are on the bar graph? ____

How many quarts are on the bar graph? ____

④ **Subtract.**

11	12	4	13	10	14
- 2	- 6	- 2	- 4	- 5	- 6

12	6	10	5	11	15
- 8	- 3	- 3	- 4	- 4	- 7

NUMBER SEQUENCE

① **Put an X on the numbers that are not in sequence.**

2   4   6   9   10   12   14   16   17

20 22 23 26 28 29 32 34 36

38 41 42 44 47 48 50 51 54

② **Write the fraction that shows what part is shaded.**

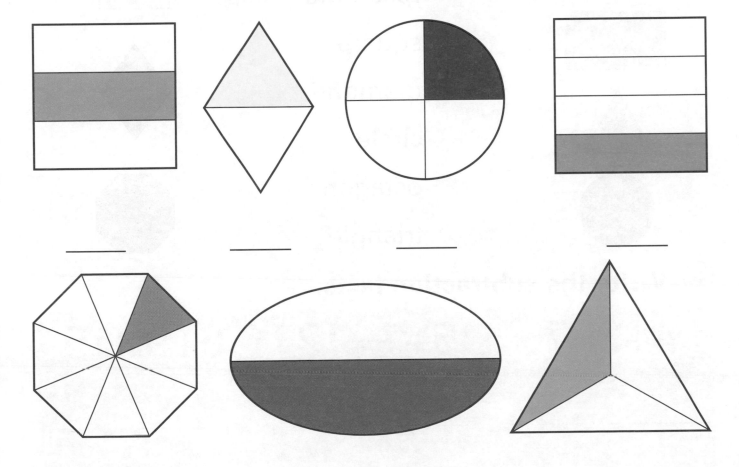

_____   _____   _____   _____

_____   _____   _____

③ **Write < or > between each set.**

186 ___ 159   173 ___ 191

135 ___ 142   168 ___ 114

127 ___ 103   121 ___ 130

④ **Draw a line to match the shape to its name.**

oval

rectangle

square

diamond

circle

octagon

triangle

⑤ **Write the subtraction facts.**

4+3=7   5+7=12   6+9=15

_____   _____   _____

_____   _____   _____

⑥ Add.

$$
\begin{array}{r} 6 \\ 2 \\ +4 \\ \hline \end{array}
\qquad
\begin{array}{r} 4 \\ 3 \\ +5 \\ \hline \end{array}
\qquad
\begin{array}{r} 3 \\ 3 \\ +9 \\ \hline \end{array}
\qquad
\begin{array}{r} 1 \\ 6 \\ +6 \\ \hline \end{array}
\qquad
\begin{array}{r} 2 \\ 3 \\ +8 \\ \hline \end{array}
\qquad
\begin{array}{r} 5 \\ 1 \\ +7 \\ \hline \end{array}
$$

$$
\begin{array}{r} 2 \\ 4 \\ +8 \\ \hline \end{array}
\qquad
\begin{array}{r} 3 \\ 5 \\ +5 \\ \hline \end{array}
\qquad
\begin{array}{r} 5 \\ 2 \\ +4 \\ \hline \end{array}
\qquad
\begin{array}{r} 2 \\ 2 \\ +9 \\ \hline \end{array}
\qquad
\begin{array}{r} 4 \\ 4 \\ +7 \\ \hline \end{array}
\qquad
\begin{array}{r} 6 \\ 1 \\ +6 \\ \hline \end{array}
$$

$$
\begin{array}{r} 45 \\ +21 \\ \hline \end{array}
\qquad
\begin{array}{r} 10 \\ +14 \\ \hline \end{array}
\qquad
\begin{array}{r} 53 \\ +46 \\ \hline \end{array}
\qquad
\begin{array}{r} 25 \\ +13 \\ \hline \end{array}
\qquad
\begin{array}{r} 48 \\ +10 \\ \hline \end{array}
\qquad
\begin{array}{r} 15 \\ +70 \\ \hline \end{array}
$$

$$
\begin{array}{r} 138 \\ +421 \\ \hline \end{array}
\qquad
\begin{array}{r} 230 \\ +718 \\ \hline \end{array}
\qquad
\begin{array}{r} 716 \\ +223 \\ \hline \end{array}
\qquad
\begin{array}{r} 701 \\ +123 \\ \hline \end{array}
\qquad
\begin{array}{r} 142 \\ +856 \\ \hline \end{array}
$$

Subtract.

12 − 3	11 − 3	16 − 7	10 − 2	14 − 9	13 − 5
14 − 7	10 − 6	15 − 9	12 − 7	11 − 5	17 − 8
15 − 8	11 − 6	13 − 8	12 − 5	10 − 7	16 − 9
12 − 4	14 − 8	10 − 8	13 − 6	11 − 8	13 − 9
10 − 4	17 − 9	15 − 6	11 − 9	10 − 1	18 − 9

DOZEN

1 How many eggs in a dozen? _____

Put an X on one dozen.

2 Write the name of each shape.

_____

_____

_____

_____

3 Put an X on the numbers that are not in sequence.

21 23 25 28 29 31 33 35 37

39 40 43 46 47 49 52 53 55

57 59 60 63 65 66 69 71 73

4 Tyler has 16 grapes for lunch. He gave 8 of them to Bob. Tyler had how many grapes left?

Janice had 12 blue marbles and 5 red marbles. Janice has how many more blue marbles than red marbles?

The children saw 17 black bears and 21 polar bears at the zoo. How many bears did the children see at the zoo?

5 **Write the missing numbers.**

154 ___ ___ 160 ___ 164

166 ___ ___ 172 ___ ___

178 ___ ___ ___ 186 ___

___ 192 ___ ___ ___ 200

TIME

① **Write the correct time.**

: : : :

: : : :

② **Write the next three numbers.**

| 12 | 14 | 16 | ___ | ___ | ___ |

| 23 | 25 | 27 | ___ | ___ | ___ |

③ **Write the subtraction facts.**

3+8=11   5+4=9   9+7=16

___   ___   ___

___   ___   ___

89

(4) **Add.**

2	5	4	1	8	4
5	3	1	6	1	2
+4	+7	+6	+5	+3	+8

47	71	51	20	67	30
+51	+20	+17	+54	+30	+16

(5) **Subtract.**

2	9	16	14	4	13
- 2	- 5	- 7	- 6	- 1	- 4

17	4	15	3	12	11
- 9	- 3	- 8	- 1	- 5	- 6

90

SEQUENCE OF EVENTS

① **Number the pictures in the correct order.**

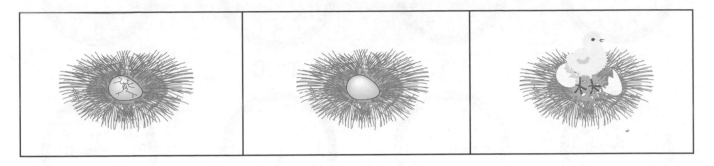

_____ _____ _____

② **Write the numbers.**

3 tens = _____   7 hundreds = _____

5 tens = _____   2 hundreds = _____

8 tens = _____   9 hundreds = _____

4 tens = _____   6 hundreds = _____

③ **Draw a line to match the container to its name.**

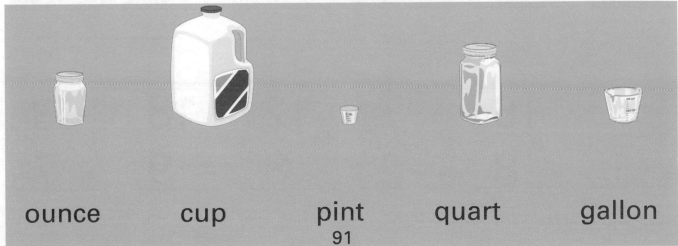

ounce   cup   pint   quart   gallon

④ **Draw the short (hour) hand.**

2:45

4:15

1:00

7:45

9:15

10:45

3:30

6:15

⑤ **Subtract.**

11	12	13	10	17	15
- 8	- 7	- 6	- 4	- 8	- 7

17	14	6	10	15	11
- 9	- 8	- 6	- 7	- 9	- 3

9	16	7	12	18	13
- 1	- 8	- 2	- 8	- 9	- 7

TEST 12

1 **Write the numbers.** 18 pts. for this exercise.

654 =____ + ____ + ____   465 =____ + ____ + ____

138 =____ + ____ + ____   873 =____ + ____ + ____

589 =____ + ____ + ____   210 =____ + ____ + ____

2 **Draw a line to match the shape to its name.** 7 pts.

octagon

square

rectangle

triangle

oval

circle

diamond

3 **Write the answers.** 3 pts.

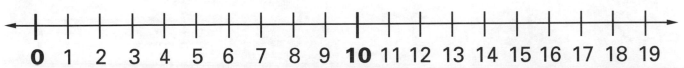

Is 6 closer to 0 or 10? ____

Is 8 closer to 0 or 10 ____

Is 3 closer to 0 or 10 ? ____

93

4 Add. 11 pts.

3	4	2	7	3	4
2	2	5	2	5	1
+7	+9	+4	+5	+6	+8

120	512	106	371	283
+324	+364	+731	+618	+111

5 Subtract. 12 pts.

16	13	11	12	10	14
- 7	- 6	- 5	- 9	- 3	- 8

12	15	13	11	12	11
- 6	- 9	- 8	- 8	- 3	- 7

51 pts. Total

94

ODD NUMBERS

(1) **Circle the odd number in each set.**

16 19	23 28	74 77	52 55
30 31	87 88	5 6	61 64

(2) **Number the pictures in the correct order.**

_____   _____   _____

(3) **Draw both hands on the clock.**

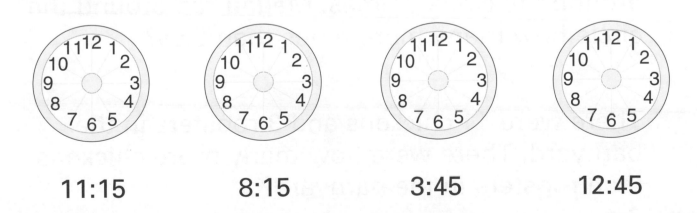

11:15   8:15   3:45   12:45

95

4 **Write the name.**

_____

_____

_____

_____

5 **Write the numbers.**

4 hundreds 6 tens 5 one = _____ + _____ + _____ = _____

7 hundreds 3 tens 1 one = _____ + _____ + _____ = _____

1 hundred 2 tens 6 ones = _____ + _____ + _____ = _____

8 hundreds 0 tens 9 one = _____ + _____ + _____ = _____

6 Megan ran around the circle 12 times. Lisa ran around the circle 8 times. Megan ran around the circle how many more times than Lisa?

There were 11 chickens and 3 roosters in the barnyard. There were how many more chickens than roosters in the barnyard?

SOLIDS

① **Draw a line to match the solid to its name.**

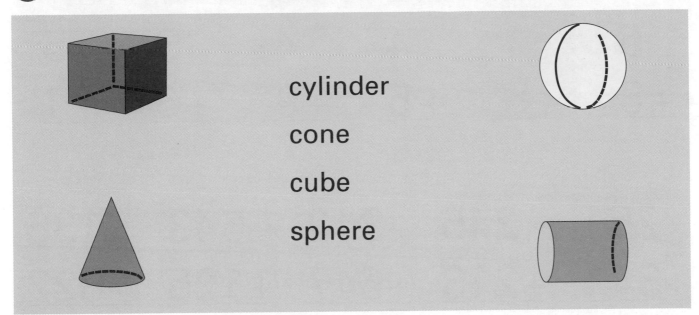

cylinder

cone

cube

sphere

② **Write the numbers.**

385 = ___ + ___ + ___   700 + 40 + 8 = ___

476 = ___ + ___ + ___   200 + 50 + 4 = ___

527 = ___ + ___ + ___   600 + 00 + 3 = ___

③ **Write the numbers.**

| 160 | ___ | ___ | ___ | 164 | ___ |

| ___ | ___ | ___ | 169 | ___ | ___ |

| ___ | 173 | ___ | ___ | ___ | 177 |

④ **Add.**

2	5	2	3	1	4
6	1	4	4	3	5
+8	+5	+5	+9	+6	+1

251	245	312	643	136
+341	+213	+647	+125	+822

⑤ **Subtract.**

10	11	14	9	12	15
- 5	- 2	- 5	- 3	- 4	- 7

16	7	11	13	10	14
- 9	- 7	- 5	- 5	- 6	- 7

98

MONEY

1 **Add the money.**

  = _____ ¢   = _____ ¢

  = _____ ¢ = _____ ¢

 = _____ ¢ = _____ ¢

Total _____ ¢   Total _____ ¢

   = _____ ¢ = _____ ¢

     = _____ ¢    = _____ ¢

    = _____ ¢   = _____ ¢

Total _____ ¢   Total _____ ¢

2 **Write cube, cone, sphere, or cylinder on the lines.**

 _____   _____

 _____   _____

99

③ **Write the numbers.**

one hundred seventy-eight _____

one hundred forty _____

one hundred six _____

④ **Add.**

16	42	43	61	52	26
+10	+52	+41	+14	+43	+43

74	21	53	50	38	40
+22	+67	+14	+24	+50	+12

⑤ **Subtract.**

13	11	15	8	12	6
- 4	- 2	- 6	- 3	- 5	- 4

7	10	12	13	11	16
- 5	- 4	- 8	- 8	- 6	- 8

SHOW YOUR SKILLS

(1) **Write the missing numbers.**

177 ___ ___ 180 ___ ___

183 ___ 185 ___ ___ ___

___ 190 ___ ___ ___ 194

___ ___ ___ 198 ___ ___

(2) **Write the numbers.**

one hundred thirty-one _____

one hundred twenty _____

one hundred nineteen _____

one hundred two _____

one hundred sixty-four _____

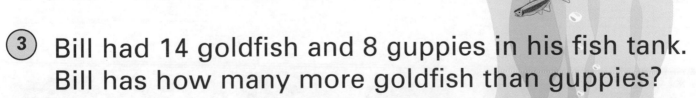

(3) Bill had 14 goldfish and 8 guppies in his fish tank. Bill has how many more goldfish than guppies?

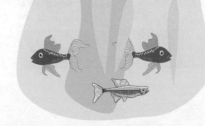

④ Add the money.

= _____ ¢

= _____ ¢

= _____ ¢

Total _____ ¢

= _____ ¢

= _____ ¢

= _____ ¢

Total _____ ¢

⑤ Add.

12	86	81	27	95	24
+91	+93	+25	+82	+92	+94

44	45	36	53	52	60
+63	+80	+92	+51	+73	+65

73	81	82	58	73	97
+73	+37	+65	+91	+44	+21

ESTIMATION

(1) **Circle the animal that is about 8 inches tall.**

Circle the animal that is about 2 inches long.

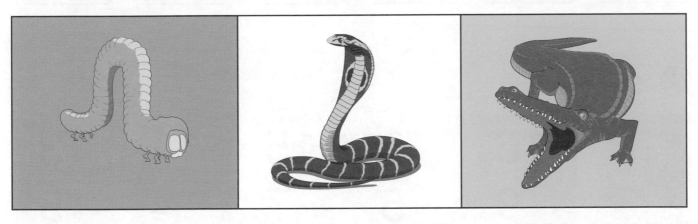

(2) **Add the money.**

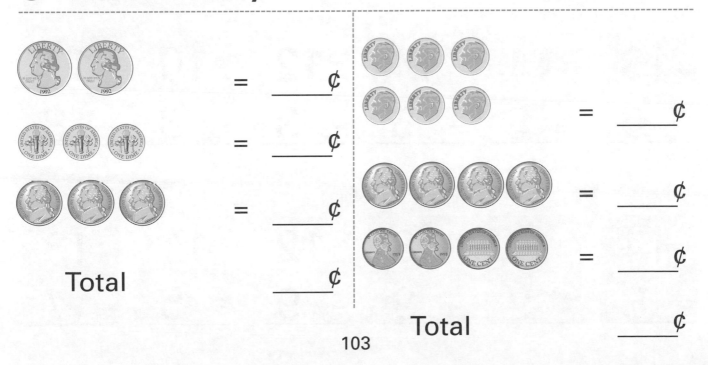

= _____ ¢

= _____ ¢

= _____ ¢

Total _____ ¢

= _____ ¢

= _____ ¢

= _____ ¢

Total _____ ¢

③ **Add.**

56 +72	43 +86	21 +95	83 +72	62 +81	77 +90

91 +48	82 +35	54 +83	55 +93	93 +63	67 +41

④ **Subtract.**

12 - 7	16 - 9	10 - 5	15 - 7	11 - 4	13 - 5

13 - 6	11 - 8	14 - 5	12 - 3	10 - 3	17 - 8

14 - 8	10 - 9	18 - 9	12 - 9	11 - 5	13 - 7

NUMBER SEQUENCE

① **Write the next three numbers.**

4	7	10			
3	6	9			
5	8	11			

② **Write the answers.**

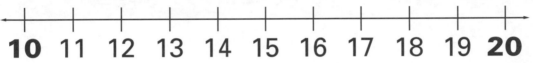

$$10 \quad 11 \quad 12 \quad 13 \quad 14 \quad 15 \quad 16 \quad 17 \quad 18 \quad 19 \quad \textbf{20}$$

Is 16 closer to 10 or 20? _____

Is 12 closer to 10 or 20? _____

Is 18 closer to 10 or 20? _____

Is 14 closer to 10 or 20? _____

③ **Count each set. Write the number.**

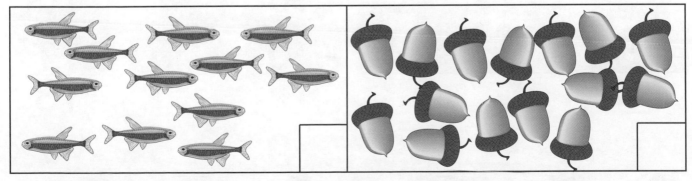

4 Write the correct letter in the blank.

5	6	7	8	9	10	11	12

13	14	15	16	17	18

$$\frac{I}{7+4=} \qquad \frac{O}{6+8=} \qquad \frac{P}{5+1=} \qquad \frac{M}{8+7=} \qquad \frac{C}{5+8=}$$

$$\frac{N}{7+2=} \qquad \frac{S}{3+2=} \qquad \frac{S}{7+5=} \qquad \frac{I}{5+3=} \qquad \frac{R}{4+3=}$$

$$\frac{I}{7+9=} \qquad \frac{G}{6+4=} \qquad \frac{N}{8+9=} \qquad \frac{G}{9+9=}$$

5 Subtract.

15	12	13	11	16	10
- 8	- 4	- 9	- 7	- 7	- 2

9	11	8	10	7	10
- 5	- 9	- 4	- 6	- 5	- 1

106

SHAPES

① **Draw a line to match the shape to its name.**

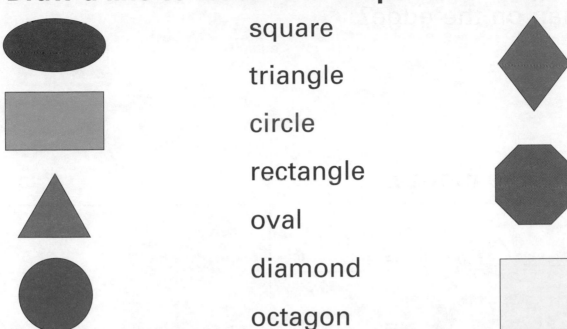

square

triangle

circle

rectangle

oval

diamond

octagon

② **Circle every fourth number after 7.**

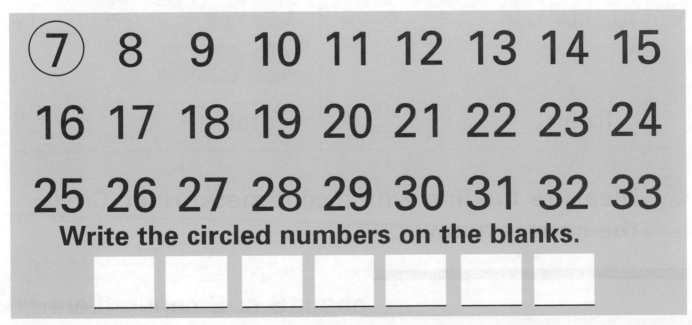

7 8 9 10 11 12 13 14 15

16 17 18 19 20 21 22 23 24

25 26 27 28 29 30 31 32 33

Write the circled numbers on the blanks.

___ ___ ___ ___ ___ ___ ___

③ June had 30¢ in her left pocket and 20¢ in her right pocket. How many cents did June have?

There were 13 children swimming in a pool. There were 8 children sitting on the edge of the pool. How many more children were in the pool than on the edge?

④ **Add the money.**

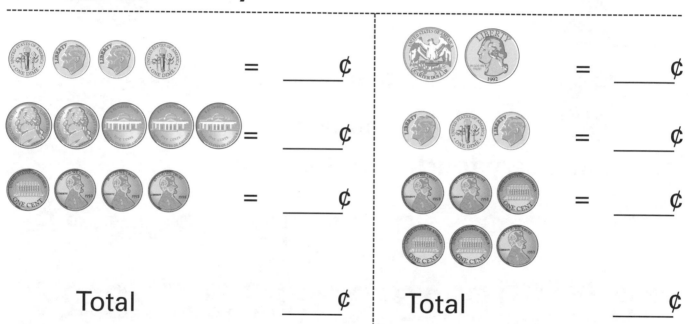

= _____ ¢

= _____ ¢

= _____ ¢

Total _____ ¢

= _____ ¢

= _____ ¢

= _____ ¢

Total _____ ¢

⑤ **Measure the line with a centimeter ruler. Circle the correct answer.**

about **8** or **9** centimeters

about **9** or **10** centimeters

about **6** or **7** centimeters

CALENDAR – MONTHS OF THE YEAR

1 **Write the months of the year in the correct order.**

June	October	December	March
May	January	November	July
February	September	August	April

1. _____ 2. _____ 3. _____

4. _____ 5. _____ 6. _____

7. _____ 8. _____ 9. _____

10. _____ 11. _____ 12. _____

2 **Write the next three numbers.**

9 8 7 ___ ___ ___

14 13 12 ___ ___ ___

26 25 24 ___ ___ ___

3 Nancy paid 8 dimes for some french fries. How many cents did she pay?

109

④ **Write the name of each shape.**

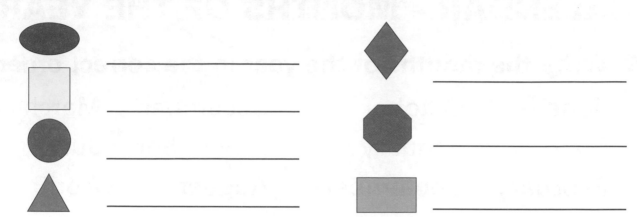

_____

_____

_____

_____

_____

_____

⑤ **Add.**

41	62	94	75	40	22
+63	+93	+21	+54	+75	+87

82	81	52	96	73	87
+86	+26	+60	+32	+72	+51

78	94	71	35	93	69
+41	+84	+82	+73	+75	+70

DOZEN

① How many apples are in a dozen?_____
Color a dozen apples.

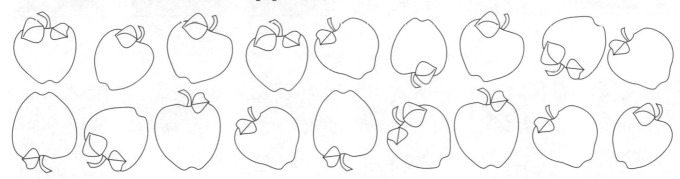

② Draw a line from the object to its shape.

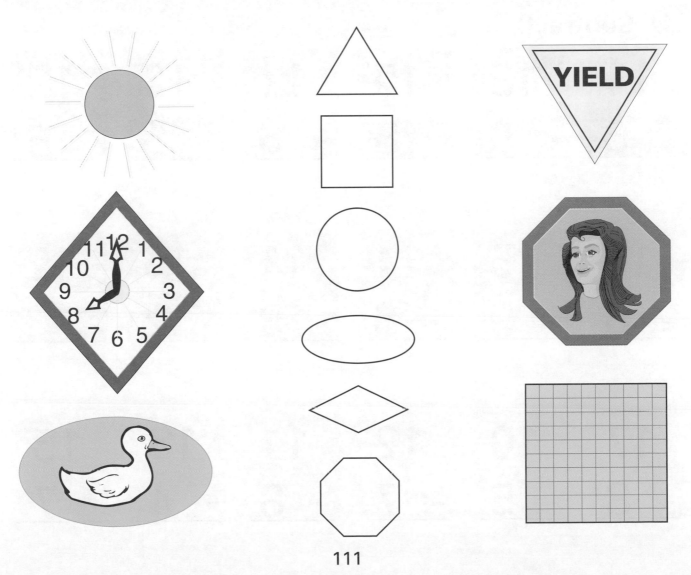

③ **Add.**

| 16
+91 | 66
+53 | 85
+41 | 31
+94 | 54
+50 | 75
+32 |

| 32
+86 | 82
+62 | 83
+94 | 47
+92 | 64
+63 | 70
+65 |

④ **Subtract.**

| 14
- 6 | 15
- 6 | 10
- 8 | 11
- 6 | 13
- 8 | 12
- 6 |

| 16
- 8 | 15
- 9 | 14
- 8 | 11
- 3 | 10
- 2 | 12
- 3 |

| 17
- 8 | 10
- 5 | 12
- 7 | 11
- 8 | 13
- 4 | 15
- 7 |

CALENDAR – DAYS OF THE WEEK

1 **Write the missing numbers.**

March

Sunday	Monday	Tuesday	Wednesday	Thursday	Friday	Saturday
1	2	3				
	9				13	
			18			
		24				28
		31				

2 **Write the answers.**

What day is March 20th? _____

What day is 4 days after March 13th? _____

What day is 3 days before March 28th? _____

What date is the third Monday? _____

3 Jerry paid 9 nickels for a candy bar. How many cents did he pay?

4 Number the pictures in the correct order.

____ ____ ____

5 Add.

64 +61	91 +63	22 +81	43 +72	91 +97	35 +90
62 +94	75 +73	56 +50	94 +54	73 +45	89 +30
87 +91	91 +38	98 +71	50 +87	92 +17	81 +65

TEST 13

① **Draw a line to match the container to its name.** 5 pts.

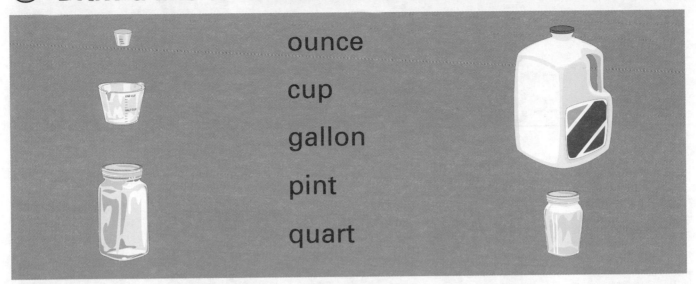

ounce

cup

gallon

pint

quart

② **Shade the fractional part given.** 4 pts.

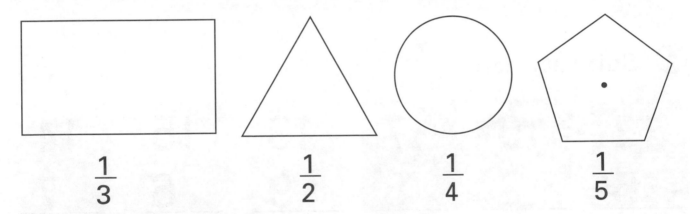

$\frac{1}{3}$ $\frac{1}{2}$ $\frac{1}{4}$ $\frac{1}{5}$

③ **Write the next three numbers.** 9 pts.

5   7   9   ___   ___   ___

16   18   20   ___   ___   ___

41   43   45   ___   ___   ___

4. Add. 11 pts.

2	2	5	3	1	4
3	6	2	6	4	3
+6	+8	+5	+4	+5	+8

621	542	714	321	136
+251	+152	+254	+463	+721

5. Subtract. 12 pts.

12	10	17	13	15	14
- 5	- 6	- 8	- 9	- 6	- 7

16	11	8	12	10	18
- 9	- 2	- 3	- 7	- 9	- 9

41 pts. Total

CENTIMETERS

1 **Measure the lines with a centimeter ruler. Write the answers.**

_____ centimeters

_____ centimeters

_____ centimeters

2 **Circle the correct word.**

52	even	odd
131	even	odd
185	even	odd

97	even	odd
164	even	odd
103	even	odd

3 **Subtract.**

13	11	17	12	10	16
- 9	- 5	- 9	- 8	- 4	- 7

11	12	13	14	10	15
- 7	- 5	- 7	- 7	- 9	- 8

4 **Number the pictures in the correct order.**

Eating an apple.

_____   _____   _____

5 Rose's mother gave her 4 dimes. How many cents did she have?

6   **Add.**

92	85	84	93	84	83
+23	+41	+82	+81	+25	+53

67	83	61	72	65	96
+50	+76	+86	+35	+74	+42

118

ADDITION – CARRYING

① Add.

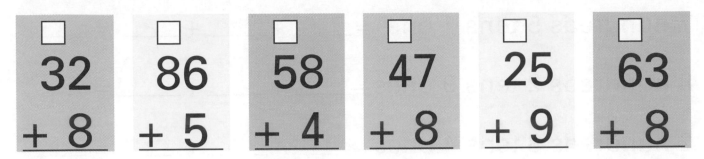

☐	☐	☐	☐	☐	☐
32	86	58	47	25	63
+ 8	+ 5	+ 4	+ 8	+ 9	+ 8

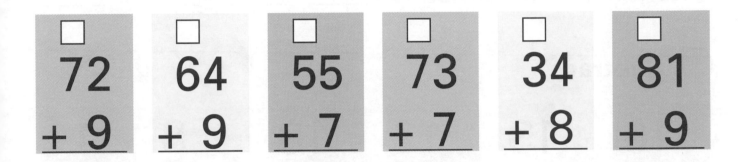

☐	☐	☐	☐	☐	☐
72	64	55	73	34	81
+ 9	+ 9	+ 7	+ 7	+ 8	+ 9

☐	☐	☐	☐	☐	☐
35	57	44	24	46	17
+ 6	+ 6	+ 8	+ 6	+ 4	+ 5

② Write the fraction that shows what part is shaded.

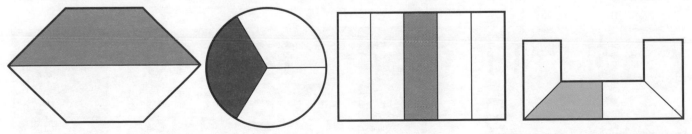

_____   _____   _____   _____

3 **Write the hundreds, tens, and ones. Write the number.**

4 hundreds 3 tens 6 ones =____ + ____ + ____ = ____

7 hundreds 5 tens 1 one =____ + ____ + ____ = ____

8 hundreds 2 tens 9 ones =____ + ____ + ____ = ____

2 hundreds 8 tens 4 ones =____ + ____ + ____ = ____

6 hundreds 7 tens 8 ones =____ + ____ + ____ = ____

4 **Subtract.**

10	13	12	18	8	11
- 7	- 6	- 4	- 9	- 5	- 4

14	11	16	10	12	9
- 9	- 2	- 7	- 6	- 9	- 3

6	11	7	14	10	5
- 2	- 9	- 3	- 5	- 3	- 3

POUND

① Write the weight of each object.

_____   _____   _____   _____

② Write the correct time.

___ : ___   ___ : ___   ___ : ___   ___ : ___

③ Write the numbers.

275 = ____ + ____ + ____   128 = ____ + ____ + ____

964 = ____ + ____ + ____   403 = ____ + ____ + ____

836 = ____ + ____ + ____   617 = ____ + ____ + ____

590 = ____ + ____ + ____   359 = ____ + ____ + ____

④ Draw a line to match the solid to its name.

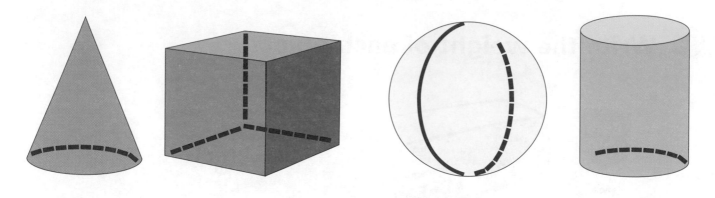

cube   sphere   cylinder   cone

⑤ Shade the object for each fractional part.

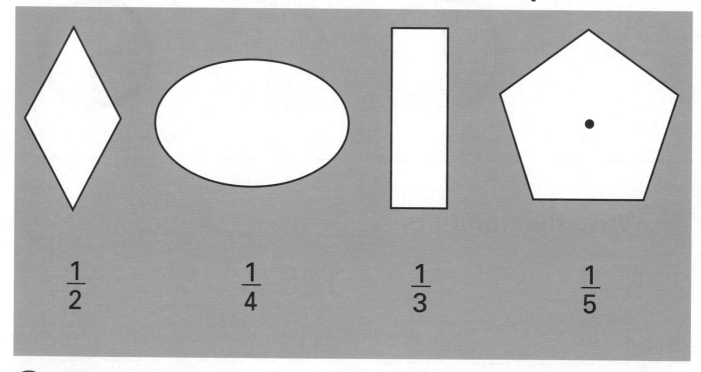

$\frac{1}{2}$ $\frac{1}{4}$ $\frac{1}{3}$ $\frac{1}{5}$

⑥ Todd is 15 years old. Dick is 8 years old. How many years older is Todd than Dick?

⑦ Subtract.

12	16	11	15	10	13
− 3	− 7	− 2	− 6	− 4	− 4

12	10	13	15	11	14
− 5	− 2	− 6	− 8	− 5	− 8

17	10	11	12	14	16
− 8	− 6	− 3	− 6	− 6	− 9

14	12	11	10	13	15
− 7	− 4	− 7	− 7	− 9	− 7

11	12	18	10	13	14
− 9	− 8	− 9	− 8	− 5	− 5

Add.

□	□	□	□	□	□
19	53	48	86	59	29
+ 4	+ 7	+ 6	+ 6	+ 9	+ 2

□	□	□	□	□	□
68	14	28	37	39	74
+ 7	+ 6	+ 9	+ 5	+ 6	+ 8

□	□	□	□	□	□
57	35	26	45	86	67
+ 9	+ 7	+ 8	+ 9	+ 4	+ 8

□	□	□	□	□	□
69	58	12	75	48	77
+ 8	+ 2	+ 9	+ 5	+ 4	+ 3

124

NUMBER ORDER – ORDINAL NUMBERS

(1)

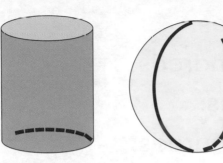 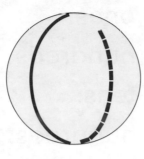  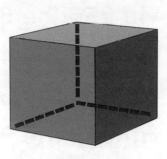

cylinder   sphere   cone   cube

The _____is the third solid.

The _____is the first solid.

The _____is the fourth solid.

The _____is the second solid.

(2) **Draw both hands on the clock.**

11:45   8:15   6:00   10:30

7:45   12:15   2:45   1:15

125

③ Write = or ≠ between each set.

In 783 the 8 is _____ to 8 tens.

In 256 the 6 is _____ to 6 ones.

In 429 the 4 is _____ to 4 hundreds.

In 375 the 5 is _____ to 5 tens.

In 948 the 9 is _____ to 9 hundreds.

In 261 the 6 is _____ to 6 ones.

④ Add.

☐
27
+ 6

☐
38
+ 5

☐
76
+ 7

☐
43
+ 8

☐
34
+ 7

☐
69
+ 1

☐
86
+ 5

☐
45
+ 8

☐
67
+ 7

☐
19
+ 3

☐
28
+ 3

☐
84
+ 9

☐
21
+ 9

☐
57
+ 4

☐
19
+ 7

☐
75
+ 6

☐
53
+ 9

☐
12
+ 8

SUBTRACTION – DOUBLE DIGIT

① **Subtract.**

58	97	39	56	85	69
-27	-52	-19	-16	-63	-51

49	84	76	91	73	28
-46	-23	-40	-81	-63	-21

74	96	58	35	95	27
-12	-71	-54	-24	-20	-17

② **Write = or ≠ between each set.**

one hundred fifty-four _____ 145

one hundred eighty-three _____ 183

one hundred ten _____ 110

one hundred twenty-nine _____ 129

one hundred seven _____ 170

③ **Add.**

```
  □       □       □       □       □       □
 66      38      89      23      26      59
+ 6     + 8     + 2     + 8     + 7     + 6
────    ────    ────    ────    ────    ────
```

```
  □       □       □       □       □       □
 48      74      16      48      14      37
+ 5     + 6     + 7     + 9     + 9     + 8
────    ────    ────    ────    ────    ────
```

④ **Subtract.**

```
 13      16      10      11      15      13
- 7     - 8     - 3     - 4     - 9     - 8
────    ────    ────    ────    ────    ────
```

⑤ Henry weighs 34 pounds and Harry weighs 75 pounds. How many pounds do the boys weigh altogether?

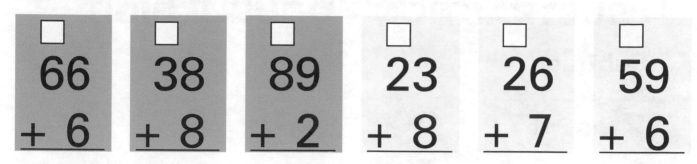

128

SHOW YOUR SKILLS

① **Write the subtraction facts.**

$3+8=11$ $5+7=12$ $5+8=13$

_____   _____   _____

_____   _____   _____

$6+2=8$ $7+8=15$ $8+9=17$

_____   _____   _____

_____   _____   _____

② **Write the word numbers.**

138 _____

152 _____

194 _____

165 _____

170 _____

③ Rover eats a 24 pound bag of dog food in three weeks. Blacky eats a 10 pound bag in three weeks. Rover eats how many more pounds of dog food than Blacky eats?

④ **Add.**

□	□	□	□	□	□
52	19	28	63	47	14
+ 8	+ 1	+ 6	+ 9	+ 7	+ 7

□	□	□	□	□	□
45	39	56	28	87	79
+ 8	+ 5	+ 9	+ 3	+ 3	+ 8

⑤ **Subtract.**

96	23	67	85	94	59
-82	-12	-50	-61	-12	-35

BAR GRAPH

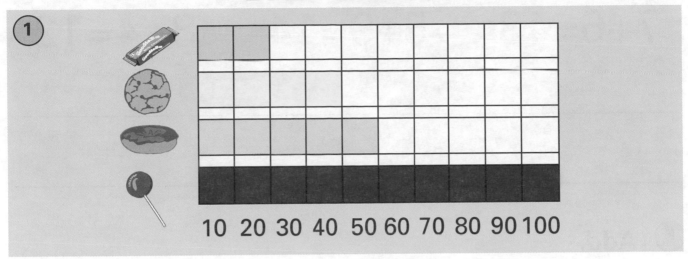

① How many cookies are on the bar graph? _____

How many lollipops are on the bar graph? _____

How many donuts are on the bar graph? _____

How many candies are on the bar graph? _____

② **Write the numbers.**

one hundred sixty-nine _____

one hundred fifty _____

one hundred two _____

one hundred fourteen _____

one hundred seven _____

one hundred twenty-one _____

③ Susie had 7 dimes to buy an ice cream cone. How many cents did she have?

131

④ **Write the subtraction facts.**

$$7+6=13 \qquad 5+9=14 \qquad 8+4=12$$

_____   _____   _____

_____   _____   _____

⑤ **Add.**

37	65	59	28	75	42
+ 5	+ 5	+ 4	+ 7	+ 9	+ 9

⑥ **Subtract.**

81	73	94	87	97	58
-50	-23	-73	-25	-37	-47

95	86	65	86	74	72
-63	-41	-32	-34	-61	-41

ESTIMATION

① **Circle the object that weighs "about" 5 pounds.**

②

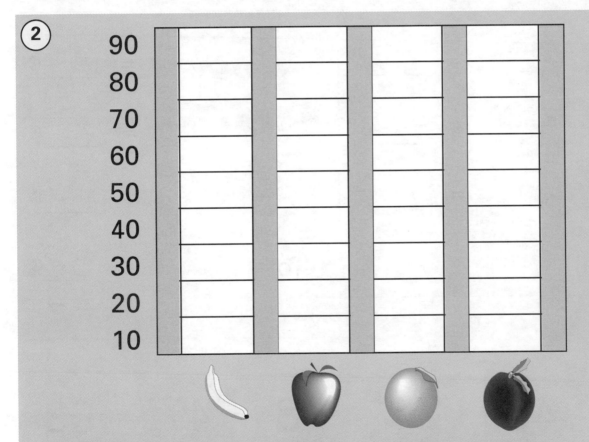

Color the blocks yellow for 60 bananas.

Color the blocks red for 30 apples.

Color the blocks orange for 80 oranges.

Color the blocks purple for 10 plums.

③ Write the subtraction facts.

4+6=10	8+6=14	5+4=9
_____	_____	_____
_____	_____	_____

④ Add the money.

  = _____ ¢   = _____ ¢

 = _____ ¢   = _____ ¢

 = _____ ¢   = _____ ¢

Total _____ ¢   Total _____ ¢

⑤ Add.

28	46	24	18	47	63
+ 4	+ 5	+ 8	+ 2	+ 6	+ 8

NUMBER SEQUENCE

1 **Write the next three numbers.**

12	10	8			
13	11	9			
20	18	16			

2 **Add the money.**

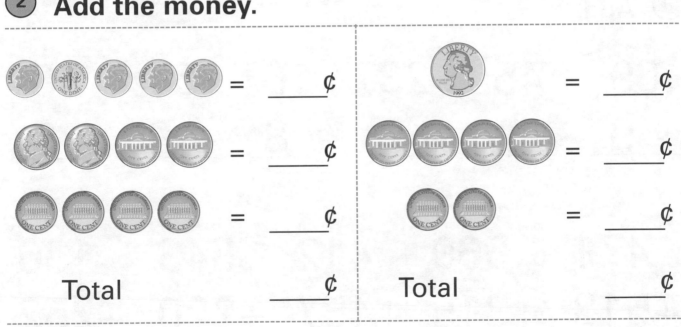

Total _____ ¢   Total _____ ¢

3 **Subtract.**

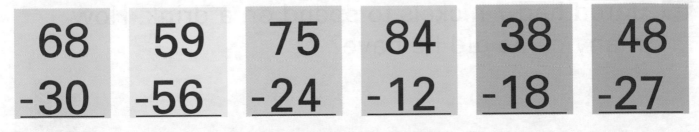

| 68 | 59 | 75 | 84 | 38 | 48 |
| -30 | -56 | -24 | -12 | -18 | -27 |

135

4 **Write the answers.**

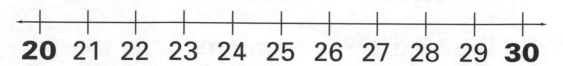

Is 22 closer to 20 or 30? _____

Is 24 closer to 20 or 30? _____

Is 28 closer to 20 or 30? _____

Is 21 closer to 20 or 30? _____

Is 26 closer to 20 or 30? _____

5 **Add.**

69	45	23	16	51	38
+ 9	+ 7	+ 9	+ 8	+ 9	+ 5

471	560	412	543	136
+513	+315	+457	+220	+252

6 Jared had 7 nickels to spend on a drink. How many cents did he have?

NUMBER ORDER – < AND >

① **Write the value of the coins. Write < or > in the blanks.**

3 quarters (¢) ___ 80¢	5 pennies (¢) ___ 4¢
4 dimes (¢) ___ 50¢	8 dimes (¢) ___ 90¢
6 nickels (¢) ___ 25¢	18 pennies (¢) ___ 15¢

② **Circle every fifth number after 2. Write the circled numbers on the blanks.**

Ⓢ 2   3   4   5   6   7   8   9   10

11 12 13 14 15 16 17 18 19

20 21 22 23 24 25 26 27 28

___ ___ ___ ___ ___ ___

③ **Circle the one that is "about" 30 inches tall.**

④ A five-pound bag of flour costs 3 quarters. How many cents does the bag of flour cost?

⑤ **Add.**

86	19	57	24	48	78
+ 5	+ 7	+ 6	+ 6	+ 7	+ 4

37	53	61	46	72	15
+ 9	+ 9	+ 9	+ 8	+ 9	+ 6

⑥ **Subtract.**

86	53	79	48	67	97
-12	-23	-65	-38	-61	-42

17	13	11	16	12	15
- 9	- 9	- 7	- 8	- 9	- 6

TEST 14

① **Draw a line to match the solid to its name.** 4 pts.

 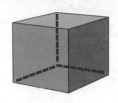  

cone   sphere   cylinder   cube

② **Write the days of the week in order.** 7 pts.

Monday   Wednesday   Saturday   Friday

Tuesday   Sunday   Thursday

1. _____   2. _____   3. _____

4. _____   5. _____   6. _____

7. _____

③ Pat bought a balloon for 7 dimes. How many cents did she pay? 1 pt.

Sam had 15 crayons in his desk. He lost 3. How many crayons did he have left? 1 pt.

 139

4 Add. 11 pts.

☐
46
+ 5

☐
54
+ 6

☐
16
+ 7

☐
39
+ 7

☐
68
+ 4

☐
27
+ 8

322
+514

740
+226

182
+607

351
+332

352
+140

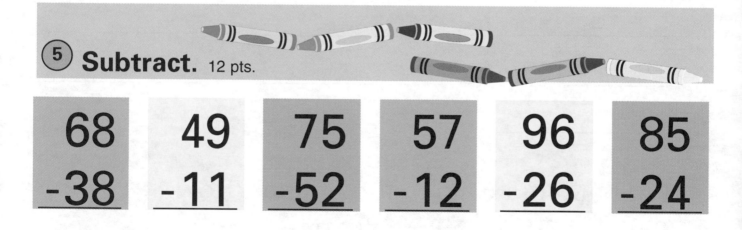

5 Subtract. 12 pts.

68
-38

49
-11

75
-52

57
-12

96
-26

85
-24

16
- 9

11
- 2

14
- 8

15
- 6

12
- 5

10
- 6

36 pts. Total

CENTIMETERS

1 **Measure the lines with a centimeter ruler. Write the answers.**

_____ centimeters

_____ centimeters

_____ centimeters

2 **Circle every third number after 1.**

(1) 2 3 4 5 6 7 8 9

10 11 12 13 14 15 16 17 18

19 20 21 22 23 24 25 26 27

Write the circled numbers on the blanks.

____ ____ ____ ____ ____ ____ ____ ____

3 **Write the value of the coins. Write < or > in the blanks.**

2 quarters (____ ¢) ____ 45¢ | 7 pennies (____ ¢) ____ 10¢

6 dimes (____ ¢) ____ 65¢ | 7 dimes (____ ¢) ____ 60¢

5 nickels (____ ¢) ____ 20¢ | 23 pennies (____ ¢) ____ 25¢

4 Add.

36	59	14	66	29	47
+ 4	+ 8	+ 7	+ 9	+ 4	+ 5

253	361	306	224	247
+612	+408	+123	+310	+232

5 Subtract.

59	43	76	93	78	86
-27	-13	-36	-22	-53	-65

10	13	16	11	14	12
- 7	- 5	- 9	- 4	- 6	- 6

6 Sam had 6 dimes. He spent 5 dimes on a can of soda pop. How many cents did he have left?

EVEN AND ODD NUMBERS

1 **Circle the correct word.**

45	even	odd		87	even	odd
173	even	odd		150	even	odd
126	even	odd		169	even	odd

2 **Draw a line with the centimeter ruler.**

14 centimeters

•

3 centimeters

•

9 centimeters

•

3 **Write the numbers.**

one hundred fifty-two _____

one hundred sixty _____

one hundred eighty-seven _____

one hundred fourteen _____

one hundred ninety-three _____

one hundred one _____

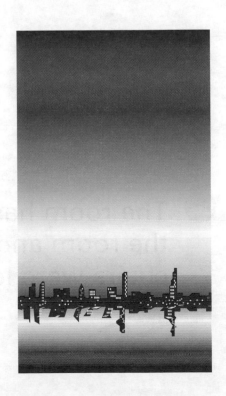

143

4 **Add.**

14	56	63	13	27	29
+69	+16	+28	+17	+47	+51

28	35	58	36	49	69
+17	+16	+29	+27	+16	+13

5 **Subtract.**

68	94	52	87	67	94
-42	-53	-31	-57	-14	-34

10	12	14	11	12	17
- 4	- 8	- 5	- 9	- 4	- 8

6 The room has 47 chairs. 25 people came into the room and sat down in the chairs. How many chairs were left empty?

144

MEASUREMENT – LIQUID

① **Draw a line to match the container to its name.**

quart   ounce   gallon   cup   pint

② **Circle the even numbers.**

16 19 28 21 43 44 55 52 60 67

14 33 41 24 12 9 75 80 89 2

③ **Write the word numbers.**

67 _____

154 _____

38 _____

129 _____

106 _____

④ **Put an X on the solid that is different.**

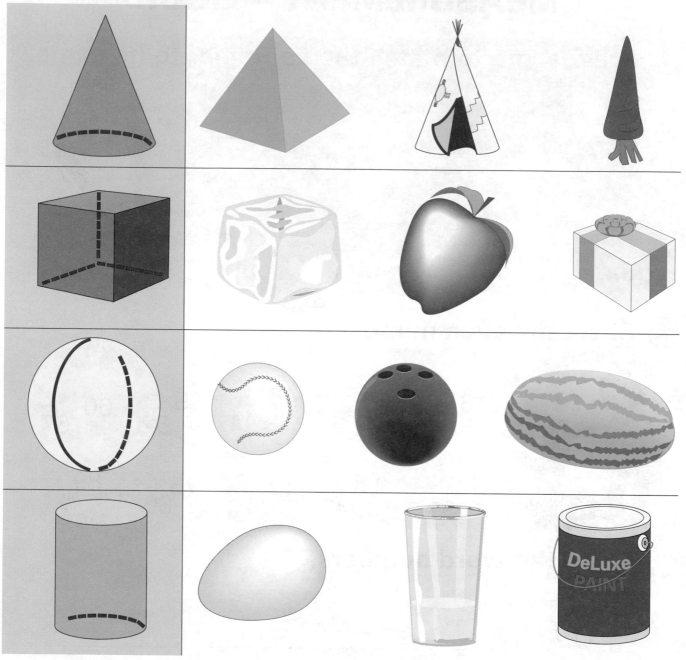

⑤ Tim bought a balloon for 6 dimes and a candy bar for 3 dimes. How many cents did he spend?

Donna had 35 stickers. Joan had 20 stickers. Donna had how many more stickers than Joan?

PLACE VALUE – ONE HUNDREDS

1 **Write the hundreds, tens, and ones. Write the number.**

5 hundreds 6 tens 3 ones = _____ + _____ + _____ = _____

8 hundreds 4 tens 7 ones = _____ + _____ + _____ = _____

2 hundreds 1 ten 9 ones = _____ + _____ + _____ = _____

6 hundreds 0 tens 4 ones = _____ + _____ + _____ = _____

2 **Write ounce, cup, pint, quart, gallon on the lines.**

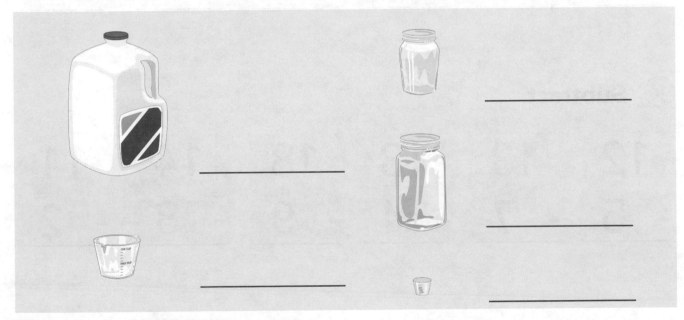

3 **Circle the odd number.**

73 76   54 51   92 97   65 68   18 15

17 26   60 57   38 23   78 13

147

4 Write cone, cube, sphere, or cylinder on the lines.

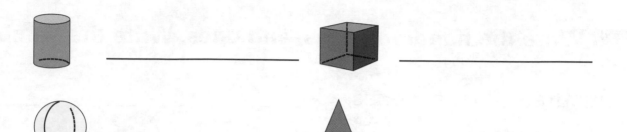

5 Add.

65	47	29	77	54	12
+28	+23	+35	+19	+18	+49

6 Subtract.

12	13	13	18	14	11
- 5	- 7	- 4	- 9	- 8	- 2

89	96	78	25	67	91
-46	-80	-67	-21	-21	-11

TIME

1 **Write the correct time.**

:
_____

:
_____

:
_____

:
_____

:
_____

:
_____

:
_____

:
_____

2 **Write the numbers.**

194 = _____ + _____ + _____   629 = _____ + _____ + _____

376 = _____ + _____ + _____   852 = _____ + _____ + _____

248 = _____ + _____ + _____   461 = _____ + _____ + _____

3 Brad weighed 48 pounds. Steve weighed 35 pounds. Brad weighed how many more pounds than Steve?

45

④ **Measure the lines with an inch ruler. Write the answers.**

_____ inches

_____ inches

_____ inches

⑤ **Add.**

32	85	27	19	68	78
+ 8	+ 9	+ 4	+ 2	+ 2	+ 3

135	714	232	826	261
+202	+162	+751	+150	+328

⑥ **Subtract.**

10	12	10	11	10	13
- 8	- 3	- 5	- 8	- 3	- 7

SHOW YOUR SKILLS

① **Write the number.**

259 has a _____ in the ones' place.

295 has a _____ in the hundreds' place.

925 has a _____ in the tens' place.

952 has a _____ in the tens' place.

592 has a _____ in the ones' place.

529 has a _____ in the hundreds' place.

② **Draw both hands on the clock.**

10:30   8:15   6:45   3:00

③ **Draw a line with an inch ruler.**

3 inches

6 inches

4 inches

151

④ Add.

14 +36	38 +45	25 +27	44 +19	19 +75	57 +14

27 +92	52 +86	75 +73	33 +73	44 +83	81 +75

⑤ Subtract.

10 - 2	14 - 9	16 - 9	11 - 6	12 - 4	15 - 8

13 - 7	14 - 6	10 - 9	17 - 8	12 - 7	11 - 3

83 -41	6 - 4	46 -20	78 -35	54 -51	97 -37

EQUAL AND NOT EQUAL

① **Write = or ≠ between each set.**

thirty	_____	30	ninety-six _____	99
sixty-one	_____	61	twenty-eight _____	27
one hundred four	_____	140	eleven _____	111
eighty-five	_____	86	forty-three _____	40
twelve	_____	12	seventy _____	70
eighty	_____	80	fifteen _____	51

② **Draw the outlines of the shapes.**

square   triangle   rectangle   circle

octagon   oval   diamond

③ Beth paid 8 nickels for a pint of strawberries. Maria paid 6 nickels. Beth paid how many cents more than Maria paid?

153

4 Add.

13 +18	49 +14	37 +55	15 +45	56 +28	29 +29

90 +73	43 +72	84 +65	92 +24	70 +38	66 +61

139 +710	316 +423	402 +267	372 +306	527 +431

5 Subtract.

14 - 7	12 - 8	13 - 8	10 - 5	11 - 4	15 - 9

11 - 2	12 - 6	13 - 9	14 - 8	16 - 8	10 - 7

BAR GRAPH

①

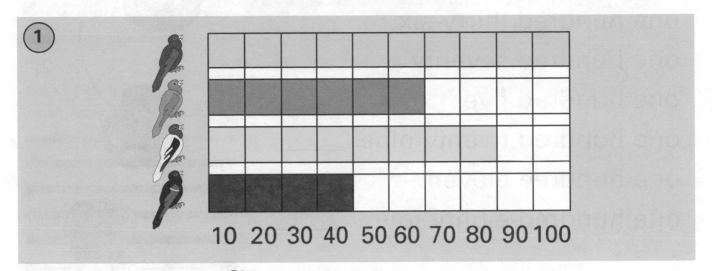

How many 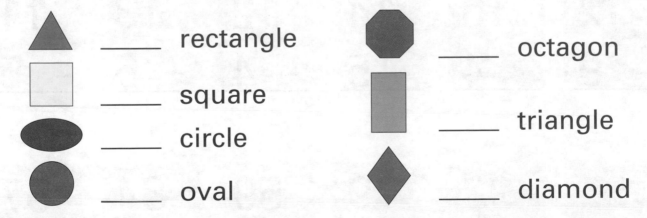 are on the bar graph? _____

How many 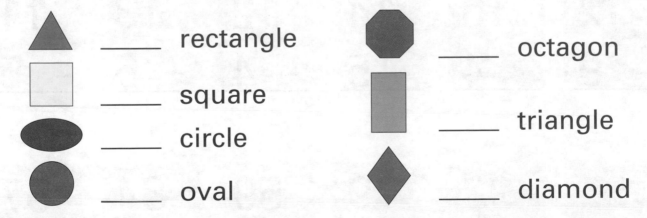 are on the bar graph? _____

How many 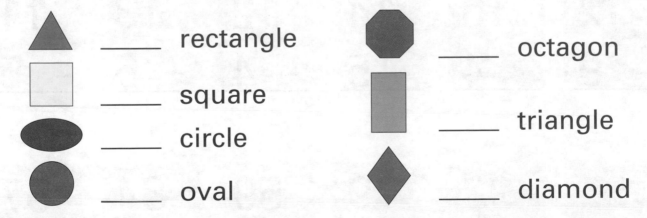 are on the bar graph? _____

How many 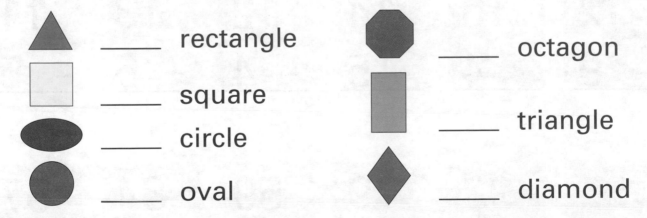 are on the bar graph? _____

② **Write = or ≠ between each set.**

▲ _____ rectangle

◼ _____ square

⬭ _____ circle

⬮ _____ oval

⬣ _____ octagon

▮ _____ triangle

◆ _____ diamond

③ Doug earned 2 quarters sweeping his neighbor's sidewalk and 1 quarter going to the post office. How many cents did Doug earn?

4 **Write the numbers.**

one hundred thirty-six   _____

one hundred seventy   _____

one hundred five   _____

one hundred twenty-nine   _____

one hundred eleven   _____

one hundred eighty-four   _____

5 **Subtract.**

16	13	11	14	12	10
- 7	- 6	- 8	- 9	- 6	- 8

12	10	14	12	13	11
- 9	- 4	- 5	- 4	- 5	- 5

85	93	79	59	84	57
-21	-52	-56	-24	-74	-42

ESTIMATION

① **Write the answers.**

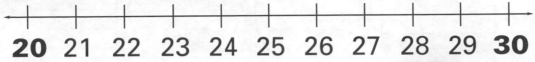

20 21 22 23 24 25 26 27 28 29 **30**

Is 26 closer to 20 or 30? _____

Is 23 closer to 20 or 30? _____

Is 29 closer to 20 or 30? _____

Is 28 closer to 20 or 30? _____

Is 24 closer to 20 or 30? _____

②

Color the blocks blue for 60 ⭐ 's.

Color the blocks black for 20 ☁ 's.

Color the blocks red for 40 🐦 's.

Color the blocks yellow for 10 ✈ 's.

157

③ **Write the fractional part that is shaded.**

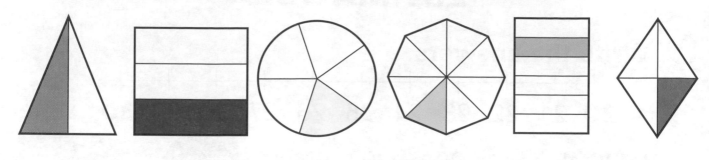

___   ___   ___   ___   ___   ___

④ **Add.**

76	29	35	58	49	36
+97	+98	+79	+59	+61	+84

77	43	48	79	75	58
+76	+89	+73	+46	+56	+72

62	56	78	47	69	69
+98	+85	+34	+98	+63	+81

NUMBER SEQUENCE

1 **Put an X on the numbers that are not in sequence.**

3   6   10   12   15   18   20   24   27

30 34 36 39 43 45 48 50 54

57 60 64 66 69 71 75 77 81

2 **Measure the lines with an inch ruler. Circle the correct answer.**

about **2** or **3** inches

about **4** or **5** inches

about **2** or **3** inches

about **3** or **4** inches

3 Ruth has lived in her home for about 28 years. Joy has lived in her home for about 13 years. Ruth has lived in her home how many more years than Joy?

④ Shade the object for each fractional part.

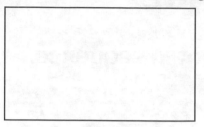 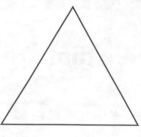 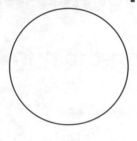 

$\frac{1}{3}$ $\qquad$ $\frac{1}{2}$ $\qquad$ $\frac{1}{6}$ $\qquad$ $\frac{1}{4}$

⑤ Add.

52	85	73	49	96	87
+89	+37	+68	+75	+74	+65

⑥ Subtract.

15	17	10	11	15	11
- 6	- 9	- 6	- 7	- 7	- 9

82	69	67	95	86	79
-81	-11	-60	-80	-12	-19

TEST 15

① 4 pts.

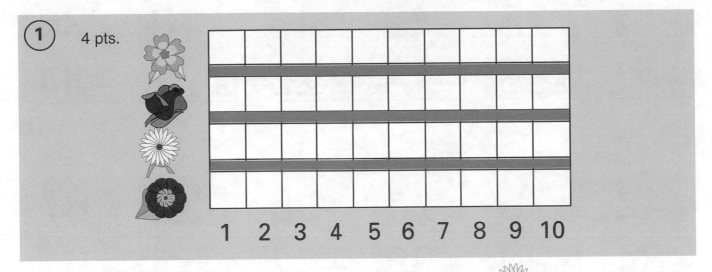

1 2 3 4 5 6 7 8 9 10

Color the blocks yellow for 8 's.

Color the blocks blue for 3 's.

Color the blocks red for 6 's.

Color the blocks green for 5 🌹 's.

② Circle the correct word. 6 pts.

27	even	odd		88	even	odd
124	even	odd		91	even	odd
142	even	odd		160	even	odd

③ Measure the lines with a centimeter ruler. Write the answers. 2 pts.

_____ centimeters

_____ centimeters

④ Add. 12 pts.

14 +47	28 +55	49 +18	46 +26	18 +77	36 +84
42 +84	75 +90	71 +38	96 +22	53 +55	87 +91

⑤ Subtract. 18 pts.

14 - 9	12 - 5	10 - 9	11 - 9	13 - 9	17 - 8
15 - 7	16 - 9	10 - 1	18 - 9	12 - 7	11 - 4
45 -35	76 -74	78 -64	68 -58	69 -58	89 -65

42 pts. Total

DOZEN

1 How many cookies are in a dozen? _____
Circle one dozen in each group.

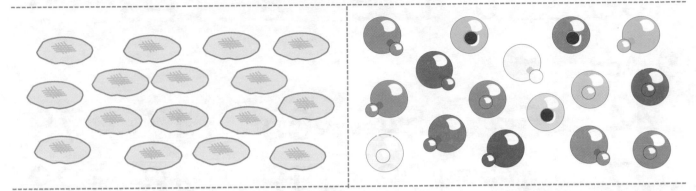

2 Put an X on the numbers that are not in sequence.

21 23 25 28 29 31 33 35 37

39 40 43 46 47 49 52 53 55

57 59 60 63 65 66 69 71 73

3 Draw a line with an inch ruler.

1 inches

5 inches

2 inches

④ Write < or > between each set.

15-9 ___ 5   12-7 ___ 6   18-9 ___ 8

16-7 ___ 10   17-8 ___ 8   11-3 ___ 9

⑤ Add.

44	56	54	65	47	79
+27	+46	+28	+19	+48	+22

82	37	72	64	83	91
+27	+91	+45	+83	+46	+45

⑥ Subtract.

10	13	12	15	18	11
- 3	- 7	- 8	- 7	- 9	- 8

93	75	87	84	96	86
-12	-34	-50	-21	-56	-23

MONEY

1 **Circle 68¢ in coins.**

2 **Number the pictures in correct order.**
Climbing up a slide.

____   ____   ____

3 **Write < or > between each set.**

12-5 ___ 8   10-6 ___ 5   12-6 ___ 5

13-6 ___ 6   14-8 ___ 7   11-7 ___ 3

4 Subtract.

764	837	972	683	458
- 150	- 614	- 522	- 473	- 138

982	746	597	658	939
- 741	- 522	- 183	- 123	- 609

17	15	14	11	16	14
- 8	- 6	- 7	- 4	- 7	- 9

5 Write the missing numbers.

0	1						7		
				14					19
		22							
					35				
		43						48	

166

SOLIDS

1 **Draw a line to match the solid to its name.**

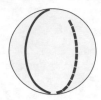   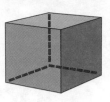

cone   sphere   cylinder   cube

2 **Circle 43¢ in coins.**

3 **Number the pictures in order.**

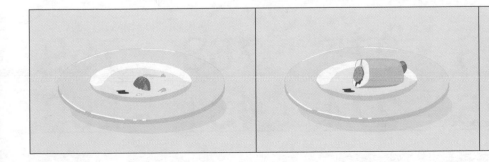 

4 Write seven even numbers.

____ ____ ____ ____ ____ ____

5 Add.

21	68	89	29	59	48
+29	+15	+ 9	+31	+28	+49

23	65	92	73	95	84
+82	+50	+61	+65	+83	+41

6 Subtract.

11	14	12	16	10	13
- 7	- 8	- 7	- 9	- 6	- 8

297	548	975	768	759
- 136	- 326	- 274	- 431	- 250

SHOW YOUR SKILLS

1 **Circle 87¢ in coins.**

2 **Write cone, cube, sphere, or cylinder on the lines.**

 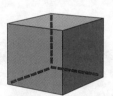

_____   _____   _____   _____

3 **Number the pictures in order.**

_____   _____   _____

4 **Write seven odd numbers.**

___ ___ ___ ___ ___ ___ ___

5 **Add.**

19	38	24	86	65	47
+67	+46	+47	+19	+28	+35

31	95	82	51	27	65
+72	+41	+83	+74	+90	+83

6 **Write the missing numbers.**

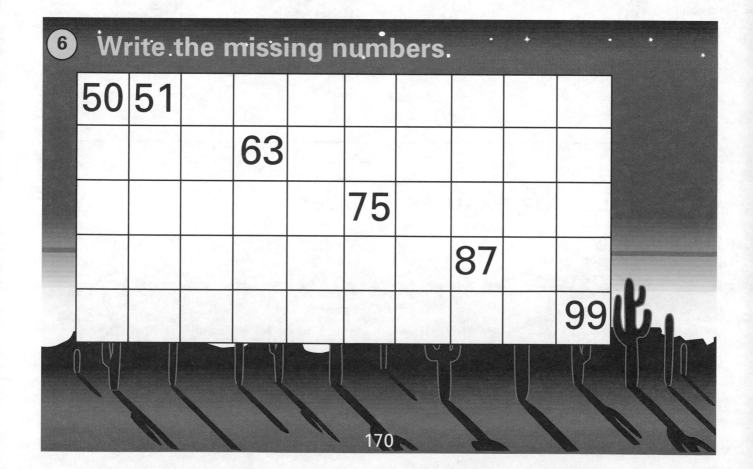

50	51								
			63						
					75				
							87		
									99

TIME

1 **Write the correct time.**

:

:

 (clock three)

:

:

:

:

:

:

2 **Circle 74¢ in coins.**

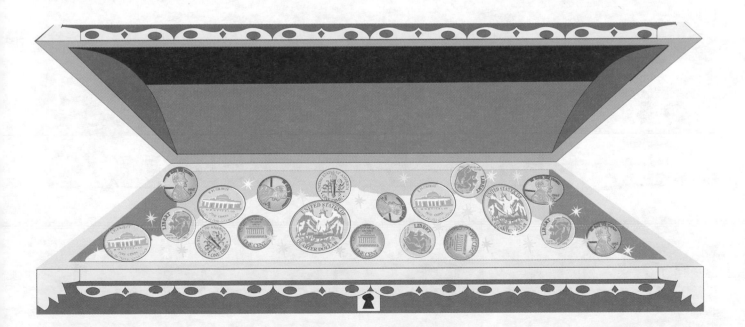

③ **Color the even numbers red. Color the odd numbers blue.**

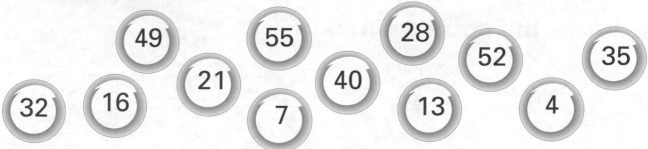

④ **Add.**

16 +64	47 +43	34 +19	28 +57	69 +15	25 +45

38 +94	75 +87	54 +66	93 +98	68 +77	87 +57

⑤ **Subtract.**

548 - 246	763 - 542	896 - 573	897 - 853	984 - 472

12 - 5	14 - 6	11 - 3	15 - 9	10 - 8	11 - 5

NUMBER ORDER - ORDINAL NUMBERS

① Draw a line to match the ordinal numbers.

4th	first	5th	second
6th	fourth	2nd	third
9th	sixth	10th	fifth
1st	seventh	8th	eighth
7th	ninth	3rd	tenth

② Draw the short (hour) hand.

12:30   4:45   7:15   5:00

③ Write the hundreds, tens, and ones. Write the number.

2 hundreds 5 tens 7 ones = _____ + _____ + _____ = _____

8 hundreds 3 tens 1 one = _____ + _____ + _____ = _____

5 hundreds 2 tens 4 ones = _____ + _____ + _____ = _____

4 hundreds 6 tens 3 ones = _____ + _____ + _____ = _____

7 hundreds 9 tens 6 ones = _____ + _____ + _____ = _____

④ **Add.**

19	27	28	49	28	78
+82	+69	+12	+21	+23	+29

73	14	73	76	45	54
+78	+96	+47	+56	+79	+78

⑤ **Subtract.**

13	11	14	10	12	16
- 9	- 6	- 5	- 7	- 9	- 8

467	845	683	367	537
- 353	- 215	- 133	- 261	- 210

⑥ Chad bought a balloon for 68¢ and a pencil for 25¢. How many cents did Chad spend?

PLACE VALUE – ONE HUNDREDS

① Write the numbers.

174 = ——— + ——— + ———

500 + 60 + 1 = ———

538 = ——— + ——— + ———

800 + 40 + 3 = ———

205 = ——— + ——— + ———

300 + 90 + 7 = ———

467 = ——— + ——— + ———

100 + 20 + 5 = ———

② Draw both hands on the clock.

10:00   3:30   2:45   5:15

③ Write the letters in the blanks.

——— ——— ——— ——— ——— ———

——— ——— ——— ——— ——— ———

second	U	fifth	E	first	S
fourth	M	third	M	twelveth	R
seventh	I	sixth	R	ninth	N
eleventh	A	eighth	S	tenth	E

④ Add.

24	17	38	35	37	57
+68	+43	+26	+16	+48	+26

63	56	98	39	65	89
+68	+87	+12	+74	+89	+77

⑤ Subtract.

12	17	11	13	10	11
- 6	- 9	- 2	- 4	- 9	- 8

797	598	978	269	859
- 185	- 412	- 934	- 166	- 710

⑥ 14 boys and 26 girls went roller skating. How many children went roller skating altogether?

FRACTIONS – ONE HALF

① Circle $\frac{1}{2}$ of each set.

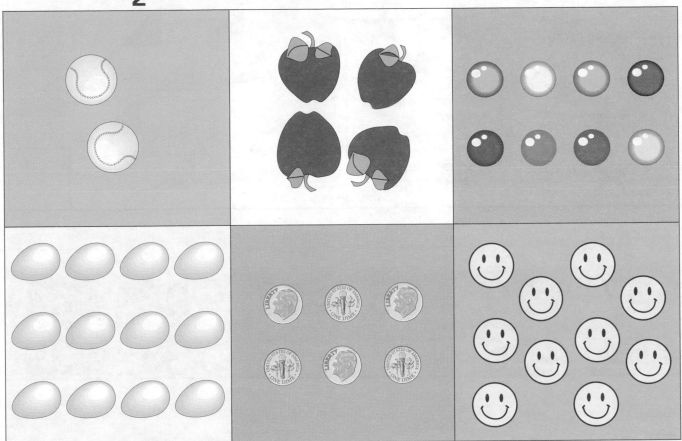

② Write the number.

275 has a _____ in the tens' place.

348 has a _____ in the hundreds' place.

619 has a _____ in the ones' place.

832 has a _____ in the ones' place.

467 has a _____ in the hundreds' place.

953 has a _____ in the tens' place.

177

③ **Count the objects in each set. Write the number in the box.**

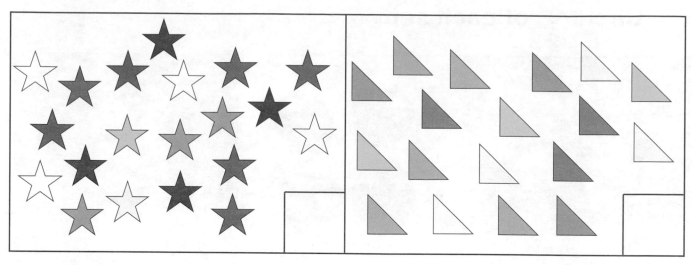

④ **Add.**

67	29	85	58	96	64
+54	+76	+47	+58	+34	+39

⑤ **Subtract.**

12	14	11	15	13	16
- 8	- 6	- 4	- 8	- 8	- 7

689	346	598	654	978
- 324	- 212	- 378	- 403	- 545

ESTIMATION

1 **Write the answers.**

Is 1 closer to 0 or 10? _____

Is 6 closer to 0 or 10? _____

Is 3 closer to 0 or 10? _____

Is 8 closer to 0 or 10? _____

Is 7 closer to 0 or 10? _____

Is 2 closer to 0 or 10? _____

Is 9 closer to 0 or 10? _____

2 **Circle $\frac{1}{2}$ of each set.**

3 **Write the numbers.**

one hundred thirty-one _____

one hundred twenty _____

one hundred nineteen _____

one hundred two _____

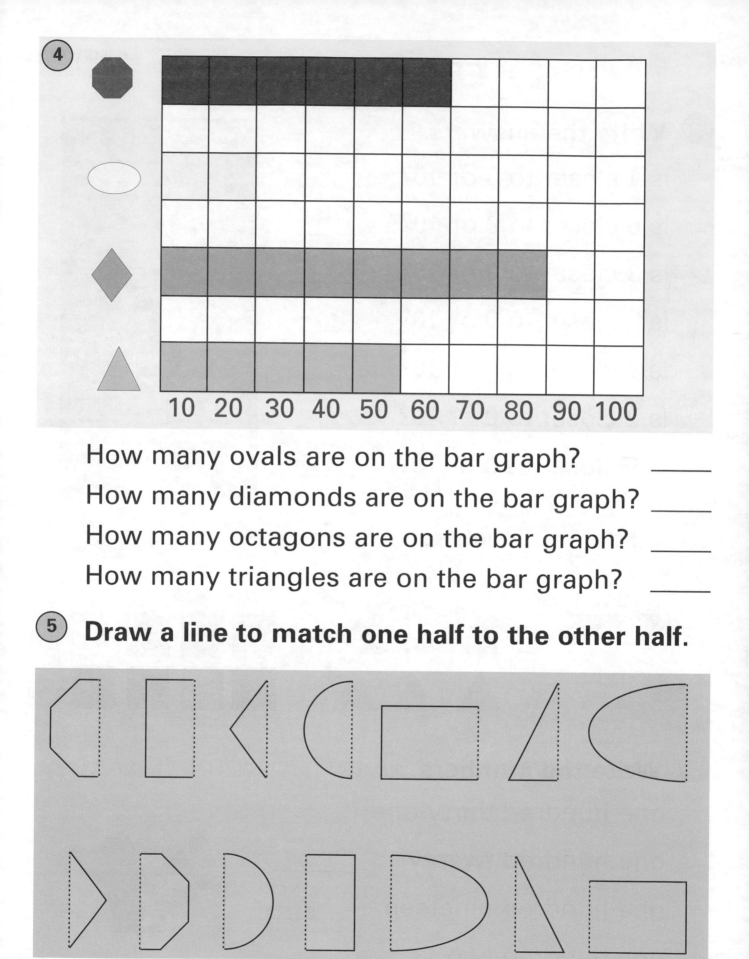

(4)

How many ovals are on the bar graph?   _____

How many diamonds are on the bar graph?   _____

How many octagons are on the bar graph?   _____

How many triangles are on the bar graph?   _____

(5) **Draw a line to match one half to the other half.**

NUMBER SEQUENCE

1. **Write the next three numbers.**

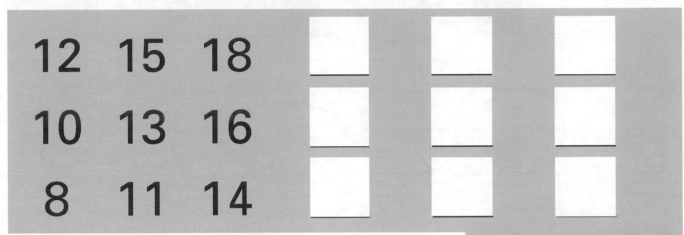

12   15   18   ____   ____   ____

10   13   16   ____   ____   ____

8   11   14   ____   ____   ____

2. **Write the answers.**

Is 12 closer to 10 or 20?   ____

Is 16 closer to 10 or 20?   ____

Is 18 closer to 10 or 20?   ____

Is 14 closer to 10 or 20?   ____

Is 13 closer to 10 or 20?   ____

Is 17 closer to 10 or 20?   ____

3. **Measure the lines with an inch ruler. Write the answers.**

____ inches

____ inches

____ inches

④ **Write = or ≠ between each set.**

$\dfrac{1}{4}$ —— ▢ $\dfrac{1}{3}$ —— △ $\dfrac{1}{5}$ —— ▭

$\dfrac{1}{6}$ —— ◯ $\dfrac{1}{2}$ —— ⬭ $\dfrac{1}{7}$ —— ◇

⑤ **Write the numbers.**

one hundred fifty-one   _____

one hundred nine   _____

one hundred seventeen   _____

one hundred thirty-eight   _____

one hundred ten   _____

⑥ Ron read 16 books in June and 23 books in July. How many books did he read in June and July?

Amy scored 98 points bowling. Joy scored 92 points. Amy scored how many more points than Joy?

TEST 16

① Write the numbers. 12 pts.

265 = ____ + ____ + ____   600 + 20 + 7 = ____

183 = ____ + ____ + ____   400 + 50 + 8 = ____

549 = ____ + ____ + ____   900 + 30 + 1 = ____

② Write the numbers. 3 pts.

367 has a ____ in the ones' place.

452 has a ____ in the hundreds' place.

819 has a ____ in the tens' place.

③ Write < or > between each set. 4 pts.

156 ____ 165   142 ____ 199

137 ____ 131   183 ____ 200

④ Write = or ≠ between each set. 6 pts.

6+4 ____ 10   7+9 ____ 16   8+6 ____ 13

3+8 ____ 12   5+2 ____ 9   9+5 ____ 14

⑤ How many eggs are in a dozen? _____   1 pt.

⑥ Circle every fourth number after 7.   7 pts.

⑦ 8 9 10 11 12 13 14 15

16 17 18 19 20 21 22 23 24

25 26 27 28 29 30 31 32 33

Write the circled numbers on the blanks.

☐ ☐ ☐ ☐ ☐ ☐ ☐

⑦ Write the correct time. 4 pts.

:   :   :   :

_____   _____   _____   _____

⑧ Write the value of each coin. 8 pts.

= _____ ¢   = _____ ¢

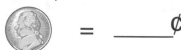

= _____ ¢   = _____ ¢

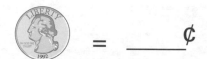

= _____ ¢   = _____ ¢

= _____ ¢   = _____ ¢

9 **Draw a line to match the shape to its name.** 7 pts.

circle

octagon

square

oval

diamond

rectangle

triangle

10 **Write the fractional part that is shaded.** 6 pts.

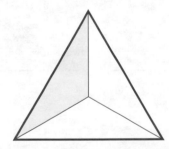

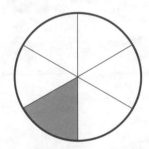

_____

_____

_____

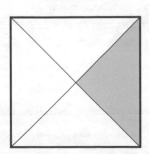

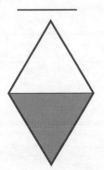

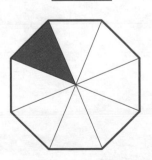

_____

_____

_____

185

(11) Add. 12 pts.

25	39	43	14	19	58
+35	+53	+27	+69	+39	+23

37	68	53	42	97	92
+87	+92	+49	+78	+18	+89

(12) Subtract. 12 pts.

17	15	11	13	16	12
- 8	- 9	- 7	- 6	- 8	- 7

63	98	75	38	79	52
-40	-34	-53	-26	-25	-42

82 pts. Total

186

NUMBER ORDER – < AND >

① Write < or > between each set.

18-9 __ 8   11-4 __ 6   14-8 __ 8

12-7 __ 6   13-5 __ 9   12-5 __ 9

16-8 __ 7   17-8 __ 7   10-4 __ 5

② Circle every third number after 5.

(5) 6   7   8   9   10   11   12   13

14   15   16   17   18   19   20   21   22

23   24   25   26   27   28   29   30   31

Write the circled numbers on the blanks.

____ ____ ____ ____ ____ ____ ____ ____ ____

③ Draw a line with an inch ruler.

3 inches

•

6 inches

•

4

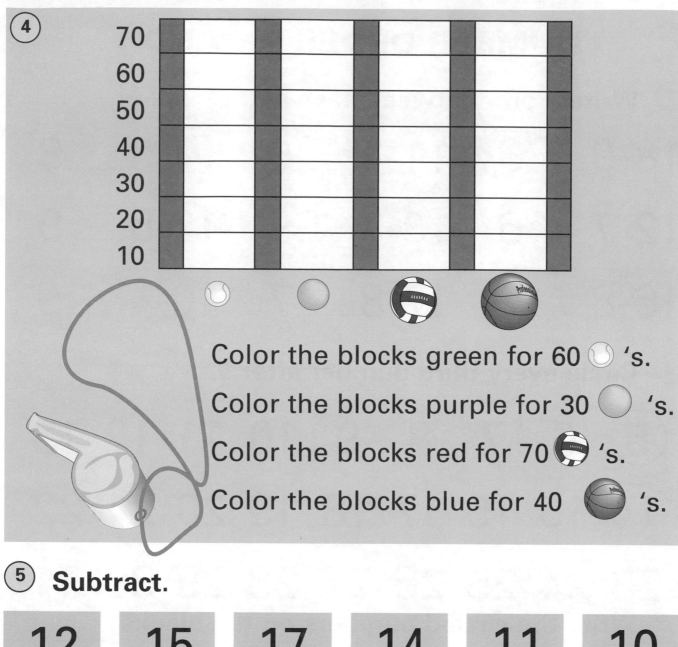

```
70
60
50
40
30
20
10
```

Color the blocks green for 60 🎾 's.

Color the blocks purple for 30 ⚪ 's.

Color the blocks red for 70 🏐 's.

Color the blocks blue for 40 🏀 's.

5 **Subtract.**

12	15	17	14	11	10
- 4	- 9	- 8	- 7	- 9	- 5

14	13	12	10	10	11
- 8	- 5	- 3	- 6	- 2	- 8

188